Rural Development Forestry

CONTENTS

Preface

Ten years ago, rural development forestry was already a well-accepted concept in other parts of the world, but was almost unheard of in Scotland or the UK.

Rural development forestry is forestry specifically designed to deliver a wide range of benefits - economic, social and environmental - to rural communities. Typically, this will involve creating local jobs along with opportunities for developing new skills; offering local people more control over their environment; and boosting the infrastructure for rural tourism.

Within the United Kingdom, many of the most exciting developments have taken place in Scotland, where the number of community and rural development forestry groups is growing rapidly. The diversity of these projects is such that it is not easy to form a comprehensive view of them; this, however, is exactly what we must do if we are to make sure that future initiatives benefit from the experience that has been gained.

This piece of research, with its aim of collecting information on the resources available to groups involved in rural development forestry projects, is therefore particularly welcome. The case studies that it contains were based on interviews and provide a helpful account of the process of rural development forestry. It also includes recommendations for action put forward by rural development forestry groups themselves.

The Scottish Executive has recently published a Scottish Forestry Strategy. We are committed to the principle of sustainable forest management to provide a wide range of economic, environmental and social benefits. The idea that rural development should be founded on community skills and aspirations lies at the heart of our rural policy, and rural development forestry provides a way for communities to gain tangible benefits and improve their environments.

I look forward to building on the inspiring work already carried out in this field. The Forestry Commission has recently established an Advisory Panel on Forestry for People. I hope the Panel will study this report and pass on the lessons that have been learned to those embarking on similar ventures in the future. Above all, successful rural development forestry will depend upon the enthusiasm of community groups, determined to benefit from local woods and forests, and to ensure that they remain at least as valuable an asset for future generations.

Rhona Brankin

Rhona Brankin
Deputy Minister for Rural Development
March 2001

Acknowledgements

This report is the result of two commissioned research projects. The first, Rural Development Forestry: Developing a Toolbox Phase I, was funded by the Forestry Commission and Scottish Natural Heritage. The second, RDF: Developing a Toolbox Phase II, was funded by the Forestry Commission, Highlands & Islands Enterprise Community Land Unit, Scottish Enterprise and Scottish Natural Heritage.

Donald McPhillimy Associates were contracted to carry out both phases of the project.

Original illustrations of the case studies were commissioned from Glen McBeth.

Thanks are due to the groups and organisations who agreed to participate in this research. They are:

Acharacle Community Council

Borders Community Woodlands

Cairnhead Community Forest Trust

Capelrig Community Woodland

Carntogher Community Association

Copshaw Ltd.

Cree Valley Community Woodlands Trust

Culag Community Woodland Trust

Cymdeithas Bro Trawsgoed Community Association

Fernaig Community Trust

Friends of Chopwell Wood

Glen Urquhart Land Use Partnership

Highland Renewal

Kelty Partnership (Special Projects Group)

Knoydart Forest Trust

Minard Community Woodland Trust

Newtonmore Community Woodland Trust

Tinker's Bubble Trust

Treslaig and Achaphubuil Crofters Woodland Trust

Strathfillan Community Development Trust

The research was presented during Reforesting Scotland's Community Woodland Conference 2000, held in Laggan in November 2000.

Section 1: Rural Development Forestry

What is Rural Development Forestry?

Rural Development Forestry (RDF) is a term which has been captured from the evolving practice of development forestry overseas and introduced to the UK over the last 10 years. It is defined as having three characteristics:

- It is rural rather than urban in nature
- Local people are meaningfully involved in managing the forest or woodland
- Local people benefit economically from the resource

It can be thought of as the 'harder', more economic, rural end of the community woodland spectrum contrasting with the 'softer', more amenity led, urban or urban fringe situation. When jobs and other local economic benefits come to the fore, it is likely to be RDF which is being discussed. It should not be confused with the rural development benefits which accrue from all managed forests. There must be a strong sense of community responsibility. Likewise, community consultation by agencies and owners is not enough.

Background

The Forests and People in Rural Areas Initiative (FAPIRA) was established in 1994 as an informal partnership between the Forestry Authority, Highlands and Islands Enterprise, Rural Forum Scotland, Scottish Natural Heritage, Scottish Office Environment Department and World Wide Fund for Nature. It culminated with the report Forests and People in Rural Scotland published in October 1995. Since then, the agency members of the group (some with name changes) met occasionally under the banner of the RDF Liaison Group, chaired by the Forestry Commission. It was this group which commissioned and supervised the development of the RDF Case Studies and Toolbox project. In the later stages, representatives from non-government organisations active in this area such as Reforesting Scotland and the Woodland Trust were invited to join the group.

In June 2000 the formation of a Forestry for People Panel to advise the Forestry Commissioners was announced. It will be considering how best to disseminate the case studies and act upon the recommendations.

Analysis of the Issues

Each of the case studies featured in this report is unique, just as the forest and community upon which it is based are unique. The projects already reflect the diversity of community characteristics and it seems likely that the woodlands will also take on the character of the communities which are taking care of them. This is in contrast to the more formulaic approach to management of Forest Enterprise, forest management companies and larger woodland owners.

However, the following patterns in the approaches taken by different communities have started to emerge.

Location

The picture is constantly changing, with new groups emerging and, occasionally, other groups folding. In April 1999 there were identified:

- 33 RDF groups in Scotland (plus additional crofter forestry projects)
- 5 RDF groups in England
- 2 RDF groups in Wales
- 1 RDF group in N Ireland

- 15 potential RDF projects without groups
- 4 special interest groups (green woodworkers, conservation groups)
- 28 community woodland groups
- 16 groups where there is community involvement

The final two groups are much larger than the groups listed. Projects where there was no identifiable local group, only an agency contact, were listed as potential rather than RDF projects. There is a positive correlation between RDF projects and remoteness. The more remote a community is, the fewer options it has and the more attractive RDF becomes.

The case studies were selected to give a good geographical coverage as well as being representative of the distribution revealed in the Scoping Study. After several substitutions the final locations of the case studies are as follows:

- 9 in north Scotland
- 7 in south Scotland
- 1 in north England
- 1 in south England
- 1 in Wales
- 1 in N Ireland

Woodland Size

Of the twenty case studies, one (Newton Mearns) was under 10 hectares in size, seven were between 10 and 100 ha, six were between 100 and 1000 ha and six were concerned with an area greater than 1000 ha. Excluding the three projects operating at a regional or catchment level, the average size is 485 ha.

65% of RDF woodlands are between 10 and 1000 ha. in size.

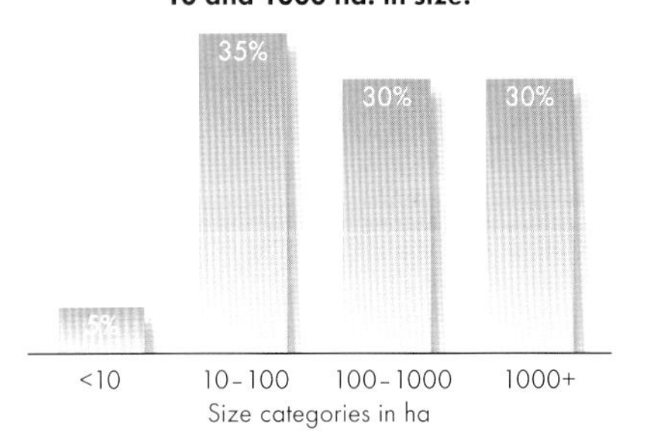

There is probably a relationship between size and level of involvement as shown in the Scoping Study. Four of the six largest forest areas have associated RDF projects where the community has taken on only limited responsibility although the benefits to the community can be great as at Newcastleton's local power station and Glen Urquhart's flood prevention. On the other hand, Cairnhead and Sunart both have a high level of local commitment to management.

Most of the projects where the community has a large degree of control, such as Culag, Newton Mearns, Newtonmore, Tinker's Bubble, Treslaig, Tyndrum and Wooplaw (seven in all) are under 100 ha. It is less daunting for a community to take on the management of a woodland of this size. There is less need for specialised knowledge and equipment. Apart from that they are more likely to be available and affordable.

Woodland Type

The woodland types are a spectrum from almost pure conifer plantation, such as Cairnhead and Chopwell, to native broadleaved woods at Drumlamph, Tireragan on Mull and Treslaig. In between are plenty of interesting mixtures such as oakwoods underplanted with exotic conifers or birch invading a plantation. There is no clear relationship between size and type, except that some of the conifer plantations are very large and some of the small woods have a high proportion of native broadleaved species.

Woodland type

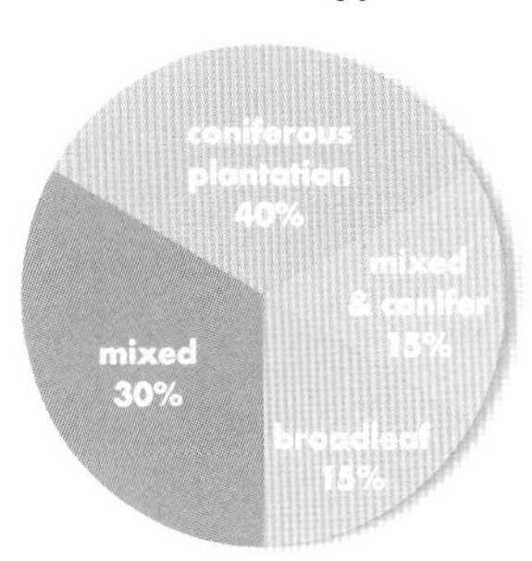

Level of Community Involvement

By definition, the level of community involvement, according to Arnstein's classification, in an RDF project implies something more than consultation. The exceptions are Newcastleton, where the focus to date has been on developing the power station and Trawsgoed in Wales. Of the rest, four groups have partial involvement, four have full involvement and an impressive 10 consider themselves to be in control.

Level of community involvement

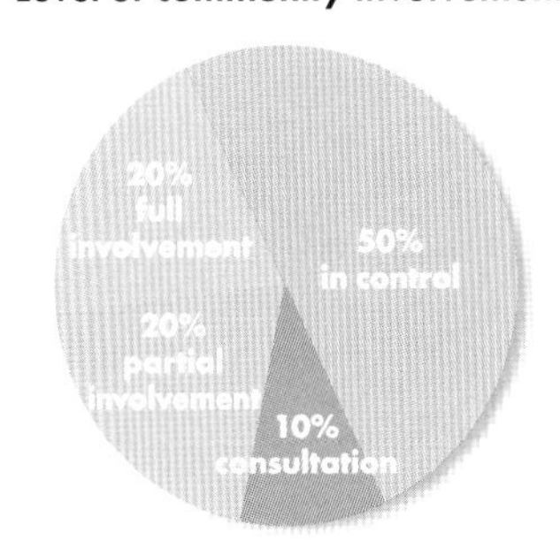

The relationship between commitment and size has already been explored. The relationship between commitment and legal structure is also apparent and is explored in the next paragraph.

Legal Structure

By this is meant the relationship between the RDF group and the owner, in some cases one and the same. Where the commitment relative to the owner is lower the relationship is weaker, for example informal agreements at Chopwell, Glen Urquhart and Kelty all of which are classified as partial

65% of RDF groups are less than 5 years old

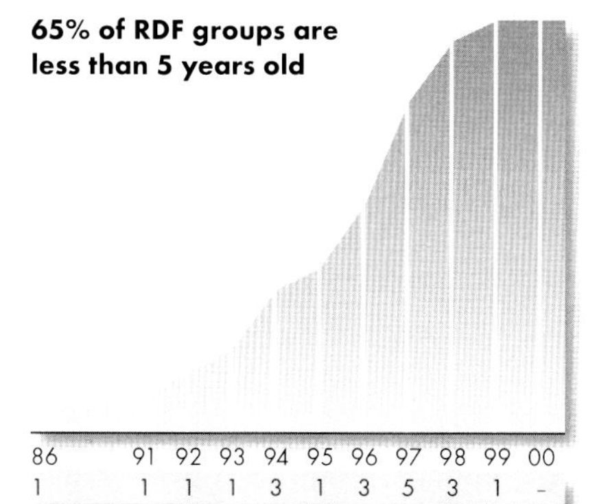

Number of groups formed each year – 20 in total

involvement. In contrast, of the 10 case studies where the local group felt in control, three groups owned the woodland, four had legal leases and three had formal management agreements or a concordat (at Cairnhead).

It appears that most of the groups have been talking to the same solicitors or getting the same legal advice as half have constituted themselves as companies limited by guarantee. There are three trusts and one company limited by shares (Treslaig). The rest are community council sub-groups, Friends groups or informal. Of the 14 constituted groups, 11 have charitable status, which opens up additional avenues of funding.

Starting Dates

Thirteen of the case studies have come into existence over the last 5 years. The average age in early 2000 is 4.75 years, skewed a little by Wooplaw which began in 1986.

Started in response to a threat?

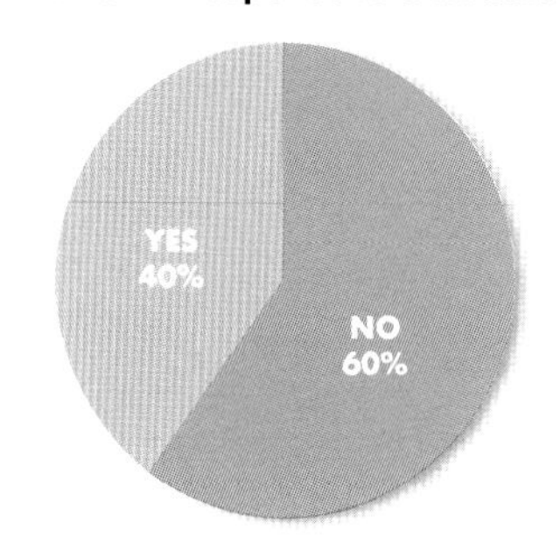

Threat as a Catalyst

Eight began as a reaction to a perceived threat. With communities operating largely in isolation from each other, it is not surprising that in a large number of cases an additional stimulus in the form of a threat was required to galvanise action. As the benefits and the examples of rural development forestry become more widely known, it is likely that a larger proportion of projects will be initiated pro-actively rather than re-actively.

Benefits to the Community

To contribute to rural development, it has become apparent that there are three main ways in which the local economy can be bolstered now and in the future. These are:

- Through jobs for local people, directly or indirectly.
- Through training for local people in order to get jobs in the future.
- Through supporting the tourist infrastructure.

Benefits to the community?

Jobs	**Yes 70%**
Training	**Yes 45%**
Tourism	**Yes 85%**
Multiple	**Yes 100%**

Fourteen groups felt that there was a jobs benefit from their RDF project. Nine projects had a training element. In some cases it was jobs or training but not both. 17 projects recognised the tourism value of what they were doing and most were very positive about welcoming visitors (and encouraging them to part with their money). All the groups were keen on a wide range of other benefits from the woodlands including conservation, access, recreation and environmental education, both formal through the schools and informal.

Benefits to Others

The others are usually the owners, public (FE) and private, with a formal or informal agreement. In 13 out of the 16 situations where the group didn't own the woodland, the owners probably gain additional expertise, ideas and voluntary input to the management of the woodland. In 15 cases, the community groups unlock sources of funding to which the owners have no access. In 13 cases, the RDF groups help the owners to achieve multiple benefits from the woods which they would have found very difficult to achieve otherwise. This could be significant if they are interested in having their woods certified. In the case of Forest Enterprise, it demonstrates a commitment to community engagement declared in its Corporate Strategy and likely to be included in each of the national Forest Strategies. In 11 cases, the woodlands are owned partially or completely by Forest Enterprise.

Benefits to the landowner? (where other than the RDF group)

Improved management	Yes 81%
New funding opportunities	Yes 94%
Multiple	Yes 88%

Third parties may benefit - visitors may come from outside the local community although in most cases publicity has to date been low key. This may change in places like Tyndrum, Newtonmore and Drumlamph where visitor attraction is a key aim. Local schools may benefit through having an ideal venue to teach environmental education. SNH's aims may be progressed through involving communities in conservation. Often there is a significant conservation element to the project and on a site like Tireragan it is probably paramount. The wide range of funding bodies active in this sector can gain positive public relations benefits whilst disbursing their funds.

Relationship to Community Councils

RDF groups with links to Community Councils

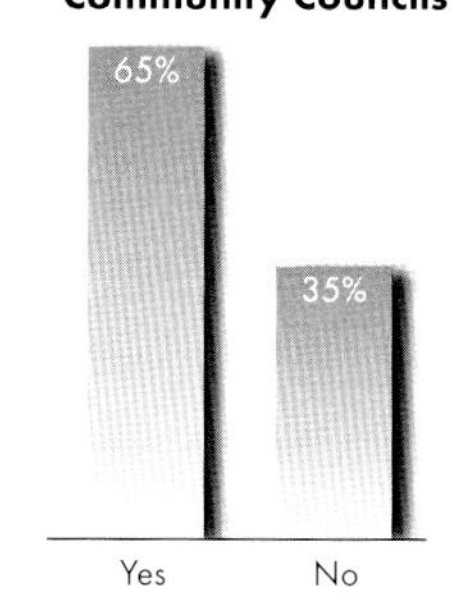

Of the 20 projects, half began life within the community council. A further three have subsequently developed very close links with the community council with overlapping memberships. Most of the projects have gone on to develop a life of their own with formal constitutions, usually as limited companies with charitable status.

Community councillors appear to have been monitoring the success of high profile projects such as Laggan, Assynt and Eigg and asking themselves whether similar benefits could be gained for their own communities through becoming involved in rural development forestry (although they may not have used that term).

Of the 10 community councils led projects, four were a reaction to a perceived threat, the same proportion as for the whole sample. This suggests that the community councils are responding to the same threats and opportunities as everyone else. They have the advantage of already being established (where they exist) and being connected to local government. Their disadvantage is that they may sometimes appear to be elitist and are usually concerned with a wide range of local issues. They are major players in rural development forestry and community woodlands in general.

Current Status

Of the 20 projects selected for case studies, four are at an early stage in their development, eight are in a dynamic building phase and seven could be described as having moved on to a stable plateau phase. One project (Newton Mearns) had been terminated but shows signs of revival. It was included in the study as there are many positive lessons to be learned from failure. It is representative of a number of other known projects which have failed to get off the ground, demonstrating the fragility of RDF projects in their early stages.

Current Status of Rural Development Forestry in the United Kingdom

1. Rural development forestry is a reality in the UK, particularly in Scotland.

2. In England, two examples were found after much searching. The first, Chopwell, has a well established Friends group representing local interest. Its main function is to raise and transfer funds from the community to Forest Enterprise to enable FE staff to carry out tasks they would otherwise find it hard to justify. This is the opposite of most RDF projects. It is a function of the maturity of the group that some of these benefits are now seen in terms of local jobs and training. The other example from the SW of England is of a pioneering group of landusers who are developing their own new community by living and working in the forest.

   To find further examples of rural development forestry in England, one would need to look beyond the commuting zones to where there are more self dependent communities with access to forestry.

3. In Wales, the situation is similar but different. The difference lies in the traditional suspicions over cooperation, quoted on several occasions. Nevertheless, community woodland projects are currently emerging all over Wales. Most are very recent and yet to bear fruit. Trawsgoed was the most developed RDF project identified but has only just progressed past the community participation stage.

4. In N Ireland, there is a rich tradition of community self-help and a strong rural character. This is a rich seed bed for RDF and once communities shake off the effects of the 'Troubles' further projects along similar lines to Drumlamph can be expected to develop.

5. It is in Scotland that RDF reaches its highest form of development. There are several possible explanations for this. The first is that there are more remote communities in Scotland than elsewhere in the UK. When alternative economic options are few, a new opportunity such as RDF looks attractive. This is reflected in the current political thinking. Basing rural development on community skills and aspirations is at the heart of the current governments' (Westminster and Holyrood) rural policy.

Secondly, there is the increased confidence caused by the success of the Assynt crofters, Eigg islanders and others. This rubs off on other rural communities which begin to assess what a greater degree of control of local resources would mean for them. Forests are the most tangible resource and groups like Laggan have led the way.

Thirdly, a number of initiatives such as the Corrom Trust, Initiative on the Edge, the HIE Community Land Unit and the Scottish Rural Development Forestry Programme have sought to encourage greater community confidence in embarking upon new projects such as RDF.

6. In all four countries, RDF is a very recent phenomenon with an average age from the initial concept of less than 5 years. In most cases, the gestation period to get a project up and running is about 4 years and so fully fledged projects are only just emerging. There has been a flush of projects over the last few years catalysed by FE disposals and new funding opportunities such as the Millennium Forest for Scotland Trust and the Heritage Lottery Fund. New projects are constantly forming and becoming known to Reforesting Scotland which maintains a database on community woodlands including RDF projects.

7. It is clear that the social forestry sector is growing and will continue to grow. Because of its dispersed nature, it is difficult to monitor progress. Reforesting Scotland with its database and Forest Enterprise which is involved in a large proportion of projects are probably in the best position to know what is going on at any one time.

8. It is also unclear how far RDF is going to go. This depends upon the appetite of rural communities to take on the additional workload and responsibilities of managing woodlands. Their appetite is sharpened by the realisation that if they don't do something, young people and families will move out to look for work elsewhere, the school and shop will close and the community will become ever more fragile.

9. RDF projects themselves are fragile. In the course of this study several failed projects (Newton Mearns, Kyles of Bute, Limerigg) were identified. One, Newton Mearns, was written up as a case study to identify and record some of the pressures which make projects fail. The short answer is- divided communities. In each case the project was developed to a stage where it became public knowledge before the whole community was given an opportunity to be consulted. Factions developed, views became polarised, words were said and the proposers decided that without full community support they couldn't go on.

10. Local jobs are the bottom line of RDF. It doesn't really matter where the jobs come from, whether it is through conservation contracts at Tireragan, training for jobs at Kelty or increasing tourist expenditure at Tyndrum. In Newcastleton, the jobs are likely to come through working at the local power station, plumbing, meter reading and banking, with the forest as a renewable resource enabling it all to happen.

11. The major players are the community groups themselves, operating at the grass roots, mostly in complete isolation from each other. Their contacts are individuals in such agencies as FE and SNH with whom they need to develop a dialogue in order to progress the project. A positive hearing from this first line of contact will progress the project. A negative reaction will either kill it off or cause the community to dig in. Some communities can be very tenacious. The agencies with an interest in RDF are joined together at a much higher level within their organisations on the RDF Liaison Group which meets occasionally.

12. The next group of organisations with which the community groups come into contact and which invariably cause a great deal of distress are the various funding bodies. Several of these, such as MFST, HLF, councils and EU funding distributors, should by now be developing some expertise in dealing with RDF groups and applying it to make applications less arduous.

13. RDF, in contrast with native woodlands or conservation, is a remarkably NGO free zone. Whilst several NGOs pay lip service to working with local communities, action on the ground is limited. The Woodland Trust has taken a few tentative steps, notably at Drumlamph where it is working in partnership with the local community. Central Scotland Countryside Trust has fully taken on board the importance of working with communities and has three full time staff working in this area. The populated nature of central Scotland means that RDF examples are few and far between whilst there are many community woodlands. Reforesting Scotland has taken on a coordinating and development role for community woodlands including RDF. A new alliance of NGOs and individuals promoting the social, ecological and environmental aspects of forestry is emerging, tentatively known as the Environmental and Social Forestry Coalition.

14. The most significant grouping will be of community woodland or RDF projects themselves. Whilst many articulate members of local groups are well able to talk about their own projects, it is unclear at present how many would be able to put in the additional time to represent the whole sector. It is vital that government and the agencies hear the voice of rural development forestry in order to fine tune their policies and ways of working.

15. Most RDF groups have a clear idea of the level of commitment they wish to make from consultation through involvement to complete control. They may not have achieved that level but once there, existing groups (such as Chopwell and Wooplaw to take two extremes) exhibit real stability at that level. It may be that in the longer time scale, community aspirations will increase leading to greater control and responsibility (so long as the owner is prepared to let go) or, alternatively, interest could dwindle and a new level would become more appropriate. When asked if their projects had an end-point, all responded that the project was expected to go on as long as the community continued to exist.

16. Initially a great effort is required from both the community and interacting agencies to get the project off the ground. However, once community confidence and knowledge have built to a certain level, the community can fulfil its role in the management of the resource with ease and the agency/owner/partner body can relax in its reduced role enjoying the benefits of increased funding, multiple benefits, UKWAS (woodland certification) compatibility and shared responsibility. As individuals, the state forester or conservationist can be content in the knowledge that their skills are being shared with and appreciated by their local community.

17. Rural development forestry is emerging rapidly in Scotland and the less urbanised parts of England, Wales and N Ireland. It is initially fragile in its early stages but stable once established. It is likely to be a major factor in the development of forestry policy in the future.

Gaps in Support and Incentives

Most RDF projects have got as far as they have despite the current package of support and incentives rather than because of it. All have reported that it has been hard going. Often it is down to individuals in the agencies or funding bodies prepared to back a hunch that the community group will be successful. Wooplaw has repaid its vote of confidence from the former Countryside Commission for Scotland (CCS) and Worldwide Fund for Nature (WWF) many times over. Forests for Real (a planning exercise) emerged from the Fort Augustus FE office and has helped several projects to develop.

The principal gaps and problem areas are:-

- Lack of information about what is possible
- Patchy nature of support from agency staff (from hostile to very supportive)
- Complex and confusing nature of funding bodies
- Bureaucratic process of certain funding bodies
- Lack of initial setting up costs
- Lack of overall funding
- No standard legal constitutions
- Insurance cover
- Limited access to published materials
- Gaps in technical knowledge, including community development
- Limited knowledge of training opportunities

Recommendations for Action

In order to address the above issues and others which arose during the study, it is recommended that:

1. The Rural Development Forestry **Liaison Group** is reconvened to consider the following recommendations and take a lead in supporting this sector.

2. The Forestry Commission takes the lead in setting up a **Community Woodland Advisory Panel**, along the lines of the former Native Woodland Advisory Panel. This panel should be UK in scope with a strong RDF element.

3. A **database** of existing and embryonic RDF groups is created and maintained. This could be linked to Reforesting Scotland's existing community woodland database.

4. The **case studies** are disseminated as widely as possible and targeted at existing and emerging RDF groups. They should be disseminated both electronically and in paper version for the majority of groups which don't have access to the Internet.

5. Existing **resources** are made known to RDF groups and made available at a subsidised price.

6. **Training** needs and opportunities are researched and published.

7. **Training** is provided in technical aspects of RDF and in community development.

8. An **extension** person is appointed to visit community groups throughout the UK, catalyse activity and troubleshoot problems.

9. This person can then **feed back** progress to the database.

10. A professional **fundraiser** is appointed to assist groups with identifying sources of funding and assist with form filling.

11. The principal **funders** are brought together in a series of scoping meetings to decide the balance of funding most appropriate in each situation.

12. A fund is established to contribute to the **initial costs** of setting up a RDF project along the lines of that provided by HIE Community Land Unit for the Highlands.

13. **Funding opportunities** for RDF groups are increased.

14. **Agency staff** are trained in a series of workshops, with input from RDF group members, in order to respond positively and consistently to future approaches from community groups.

15. **Community Councils** with an interest in rural development are identified and encouraged to explore the opportunities for RDF in their area.

16. Gaps in **advisory material**, such as standard constitutions and group insurance cover, are filled by commissioning research in these areas. Current availability should be reviewed.

17. **Indicators** are developed which can be used to monitor the success of RDF projects in terms of jobs, input to the local economy and community capacity.

Update as of March 2001

1. The Rural Development Forestry Liaison Group has agreed to reconvene. First meeting scheduled for spring 2001.

2. The Forestry Commission set up an Advisory Panel on Forestry for People in September 2000. The panel will advise the Forestry Commission on ways to optimise the benefits of forestry for local communities, especially in rural areas; stimulate greater community involvement in forestry; and develop and disseminate best practice in the encouragement and management of community involvement.

4. The case studies were presented to community groups at Reforesting Scotland's Community Woodland Conference held in Laggan in November 2000. They have subsequently been posted on the Forestry Commission website and are produced in full in this publication.

17. Indicators of progress are being developed as part of the implementation of the new Scottish Forestry Strategy.

Southern Upland Way
Cairnhead
Dibbin Lane
Blairoch
Benbuie
Moniaive
Nature Trails
Wildlife
Sculpture
Xmas Trees
Chopwell Woods
Derwent Water
Loch Trool
Newton Stewart
Lochinver
Lady Constance Bay
Loch Culag
Gortagh River
Coleraine
Drumlamph
Maghera
Glen Coiltie
Glen Urquhart
Drumnadrochit
Flood
Inverness
Loch Ness
Perth
Blairadam Forest
Lochore
Kelty
Edinburgh
The Butterchurn
Knoydart
Barrisdale
Inverie
Mallaig
Lochgilphead
Minard Castle
Loch Fyne
Minard
Kielder Forest
Newcastleton Forest
Kershope Forest
Hawick
Carlisle
Newcastleton
Plan
Nimby
St Madoes School
Newton Mearns
Housing
River Calder
Newtonmore
River Spey
Avimore
Pitlochry
Creag Mhaol
Loch Carron
Achmore
Kyle of Lochalsh
Stromeferry
Visitors' Centre
Salen
Loch Sunart
Strontian
Tinker's Bubble
Gardens
Dwellings
Iona
Tireragan
Ross of Mull
Eilean Mor
Llanafan
Tangarth
Aberystwyth
Trawsgoed
SOLD
Achaphubuil
Camusnagaul
Loch Linnhe
Fort William
Ben Nevis
Tyndrum
Dalrigh
Native Pinewood
West Highland Way
Crianlarich
Axehead Wood
Big Wood
Allan Water
Lauder
Stow
Elmtree Wood
Gutter Wood
Woolaw Woods
Galashiels

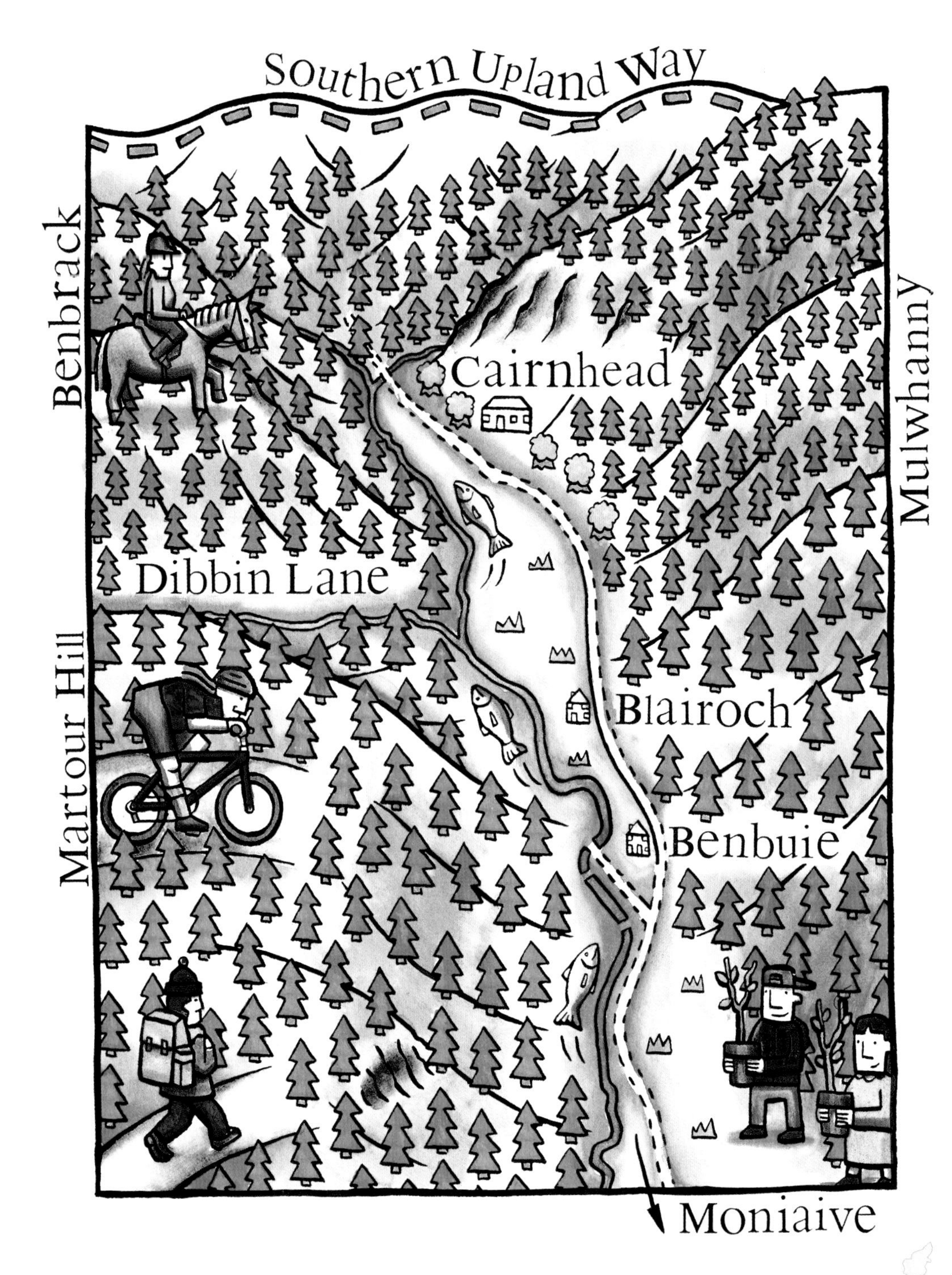

Summary

- Cairnhead Community Forest is in Dumfriesshire, to the north of Moniaive.
- The forest extends to 1347 hectares. It is 96% spruce with an agricultural tenancy in the valley bottom.
- The forest is managed through a Concordat with Forest Enterprise.
- Cairnhead Community Forest Trust runs the project.
- The Trust is a limited Company with charitable status.
- The key aims are conservation, development and management.
- The project was initiated in 1996.

Cairnhead

Why? When Forest Enterprise (FE) put Cairnhead Forest on the market in 1996, local people were concerned about the impact a change of ownership might have on the village of Moniaive, 6 miles down the glen. With the forest approaching first thinnings, the principal concern was the haulage of timber through the narrow streets of the village and the narrow roads beyond.

They made contact with South West Community Woodlands (SWCW) who were, at the time, on the lookout for suitable projects to develop. A joint group visited the forest and the concept of a community forest project was born. In fact, the project has developed separately from SWCW and has grown into a positive working partnership between FE and Cairnhead Community Forest Trust Ltd. on behalf of the local community.

Various individuals from within and outside of the local community formed a Steering Group to progress ideas. The Community Council gave its support to the project and this backing has strengthened as progress has been made and events have been held in the forest. The Community Council is active and long established.

Who? The project is for the benefit of the people of the Parish of Glencairn in order that they might have a greater share in the benefits flowing from the forest. The community is rural with many people scattered beyond the village.

Two legal entities have been set up to represent the local community. These are the Cairnhead Community Forest Trust which is a Limited Company with charitable status and the Cairnhead Community Forest Members Association. The Trustees were originally appointed, but will be elected in the future. The Association was formed as a supporters group to allow people from within and beyond the local community to support the project. There are members throughout the UK and overseas, although most are resident in the parish. A Management Group, with membership drawn from the Trust, the Association and FE looks after the day to day running of the project. It includes Peter Ross who is the Project Forest Manager. There are some 25-30 people who are actively involved in taking the project forward.

What? The forest nestles in the hills at the upper end of the Dalwhat Glen, 6 miles from Moniaive, in Dumfriesshire. It extends to 1347 hectares (3328 acres) on hills that climb to over 1600 feet. Two thirds of the area was planted by the Forestry Commission with commercial conifers (89% Sitka spruce, 7% Norway spruce, 4% larch and other conifers) between 1976 and 1979. The forest has not yet been thinned.

The bottom of the glen remains unplanted as well as some of the tops and the burnsides. There is a 5 year agricultural tenancy and two grazing tenancies on the open ground. Formerly, the land was split between two upland sheep farms. The nature conservation interest will become clear once a complete ecological survey has been undertaken. The forest is already a popular place for walking for a small number of local people and the Southern Upland Way follows its north-west boundary.

Most of the forest is harvestable with the exception of some of the steeper slopes which could be left as long term retentions. The extraction routes present one of the thorny issues to be discussed as part of the Forest Design Plan consultations which are due to start shortly.

The new objectives for the forest, as compared to the project, have yet to be set.

Vision? An exciting vision of the future forest is developing. This ranges from commercial forestry operations creating much needed local employment, to wild areas giving sanctuary to as wide a range of wildlife as possible. Further work will be generated through habitat creation (one or two lochans will be excavated in the near future) and through other projects such as a field centre and green tourism projects. In addition, opportunities for recreation - walking, mountain biking, pony trekking, orienteering and other sports will be enhanced.

The aims of the project have been summarised as conservation, development and management. Conservation of the scenic character and biodiversity of the forest including the water catchment and the human heritage. The development activities will promote business and employment opportunities in forest operations and replanting with more diverse species; increasing fish stocks; restoring Cairnhead Cottage; constructing high quality lodges; investigating small scale power generation and the provision of leisure facilities. The management approach will be business orientated, encouraging public, community and private investment in order to maximise employment opportunities for the community in some of the specific project activities referred to above.

How? A good deal of positive action has been generated by this project, started in response to a threat. People feared that a change of ownership due to the disposal of a FE property might result in difficulties and loss of opportunities for local people. This led to the members of the local community coming together to form a Steering Group in April 1997 Soon after that contact was made with FE and from that point forward a positive partnership has developed. A group visited Laggan in May 1997 and decided that they would like to have a greater degree of control and less confrontation at Cairnhead than had been the case (probably for historical reasons) at Laggan. The obvious solution was for the Forestry Commission to retain ownership on behalf of the nation, with the local community having a major input to its management by FE, through the Trust and Association, formalised in a Concordat.

The **milestones** have been:

1. The meeting between local people and SWCW in February '97.
2. The formation of the Steering Group for Project Cairnhead in April '97.
3. The visit to Laggan in May '97.
4. Meeting with FE staff in June '97.
5. Meeting with Cairnhead Community Council and gaining support in Sept '97.
6. Commissioning of a Feasibility Study.
7. Contact made with local schools and Crichton College, in Dumfries.
8. Start up funding acquired.
9. Open facilitated participatory meeting held in May '98. Attended by 62 people.
10. Cairnhead Community Forest Members Association was formed at a public meeting, attended by 35 people, in June '98. The first AGM was in April '99.
11. An Open Day was held in the forest in Sept '98.
12. The Trust was formally established in Sept '98.
13. Signing of the Concordat with FE in February '99.
14. The Project was formally launched on May 13th 1999 with wee people (local primary schoolchildren) planting wee trees (broadleaved whips) and releasing wee fish (salmon fry) into the river. The event was well covered by local press including Border TV.
15. The Project Office opened for business in August '99.

The biggest **challenges** were:

- An initial antagonism from the Community Council. With hindsight, they could have been consulted at an earlier stage. The **solution** was to discuss the ideas with the chairman and present them at a Council meeting. The Community Council are now fully on board and have an overlapping membership with the Trust and Association.

- Lack of core funding. This continues to be a problem. Project funding is easier to obtain than core funding. The **solution** is to try and use part of the project funding to cover core costs.

- Distance between the forest and Moniaive. The six mile drive to the forest is going to deter some from using it for recreation on a regular basis. On the other hand, the rural development aspects, such as local employment, will benefit from such a close proximity.

Greatest achievements? Setting up long-term, workable legal structures to enable the partnership with FE to work efficiently is the greatest achievement (and has been the biggest challenge) to date. It has required a great deal of diplomacy to identify, approach and persuade the most appropriate people to fill particular roles during this crucial early phase of the project. There is a fine balance to be struck between appointment and democracy during the early stages of any project. There is consensus that this difficult phase is now largely over and the real work of managing the community forest can begin.

Sources of help and advice? Many skills were available within the group. They included forest management (FE and Peter Ross), business management, administrative skills, PR skills (with help from FE), local knowledge and political nous.

A skill brought in by the land agents commissioned to write the feasability study was the application of objectivity to the forestry and building conversion possibilities. David O'Neil of SWCW provided another skill, that of facilitation of the participatory meeting. .

Top of the list of helpful organisations has been Forest Enterprise. Despite the community's first learning of the proposed sale of the forest by way of a small advert in the local press, the community's relationship with FE has grown into a positive and involved partnership. Dumfries and Galloway Council provided contacts and start-up funding. Groundbase (Leader) and the Local Enterprise Company helped with developing funding. SNH provided technical input as well as possible future funding. The local Salmon Fishery Board provided enthusiastic advice and help in kind.

Principal funders to date are Dumfries and Galloway Council and Groundbase, with SNH funding pending. This covers only the setting up costs and a lot more funding is being actively sought. An individual has been awarded a Millennium Forest Award and is being supported by the project.

No formal training has taken place to date but, informally, FE has greatly raised the level of knowledge of both Trustees and members of the Association. The Forest Design Plan process is regarded as being a valuable education process for all concerned.

Future activities? The proposed activities for 1999 and 2000 are contained within the costed Work Plan approved by the Trust in March '99. They are listed as:

- Community Forest Centre- refurbishment and making the office fully functional
- Participation and Membership- Concordat preparation, community picnic, craft event, planting and Moniaive Gala
- Media and Promotion- logo, leaflets and press releases
- Water Resources- water & fishing links, habitat survey, habitat enhancement and native trout fishery

- Community Arts- community event and arts groups/professionals
- Education- local schools and Crichton College
- Cairnhead Cottage- development plan and conversion
- Economic Opportunities- re-open slate quarry
- Public Access- path development and orienteering
- All of the above is in addition to developing the Forest Design Plan in partnership with FE.

As regards an **end point** for the project, the Concordat has been signed for a 50 year period with the possibility of renewal. If the community is supportive, there is no reason why the project shouldn't continue for as long as the community itself.

The **optimal level** of involvement depends upon the current level of interest and enthusiasm. The project is sufficiently flexible that it can operate at a low or high level of input from the local community. At present the level is very high.

The best means of ensuring **continuity** of active group members is by providing a wide range of opportunities for different individuals and groups within the community to get involved. Many of the children who participated in the launch day were enthused about the possibilities the forest presents for them now, and as adults in the future. The legal structures help to develop continuity by requiring Trustees and Association office-bearers to step down on a regular basis to be replaced by others or to seek re-election.

Lessons for others? The main lesson is to try to balance emerging viewpoints with existing community structures, in this case the Cairnhead Community Council. Meetings need to be open and decision-making transparent.

The challenges now are:

- to sustain and develop interest in the community
- to develop the local economic benefits of the forest

These twin challenges are closely linked.

When a group of core people were asked how close the project was to delivering the ideal community forest, the answer was 20%. They felt that the first structural phase was now largely and successfully completed. The work of managing and developing the forest had only just begun.

Peter Ross
Project Forest Manager
Cairnhead Community Forest Trust Ltd
Community Forest Office
Dunreggan, Moniaive DG3 4HQ

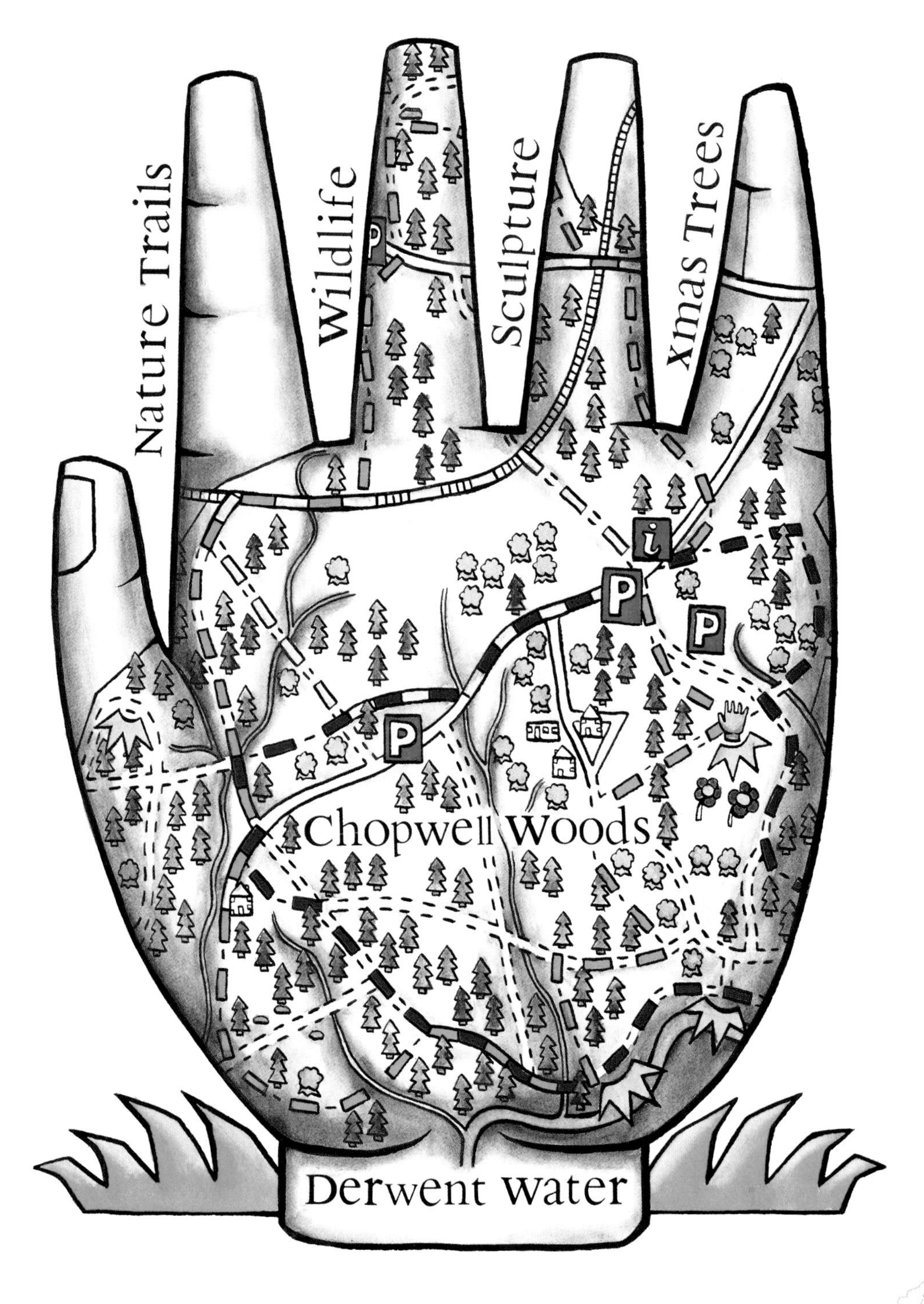

Summary

- Chopwell Wood is 10 miles south-west of Newcastle/Gateshead.
- It extends to 384 hectares of mixed conifer plantation with some areas of broadleaves.
- The woodland is managed as an informal partnership with Forest Enterprise.
- Friends of Chopwell Wood (FOCW) manage the project.
- FOCW is a voluntary organisation with a simple constitution.
- The key aim is to work in partnership with FE to develop the wood for recreation, education and conservation and to encourage community responsibility for it.
- The project began in 1991.

Chopwell

Why? The Friends of Chopwell Wood (FOCW) project was initiated in 1991 by Iain Laidlaw and Petra Biberbach who both lived within the wood. Iain worked for the Forestry Commission (FC). There was at that time concern about the potential privatisation of woodlands and also about mineral extraction in the area. It was considered that the formation of a local 'Friends' group which could campaign for Woodland Park status could be a useful mechanism for protecting the woodland for the local community.

A public meeting was held in the local primary school in November 1991 and over 100 local people turned up. The idea of forming a Friends group was put to the meeting and accepted with enthusiasm. A voluntary committee was formed immediately. It was agreed that the main function of the group should be to enhance recreation, education and conservation in the woodland. The Friends group was supported by Forest Enterprise area manager, Clive Large.

Who? Chopwell Wood is situated about 10 miles to the south-west of the Newcastle/Gateshead conurbation - with 1 million people living within a 20 mile radius. A recent survey indicated that it received approximately 70,000 visits a year (the same as Kielder Forest Park). The general opinion is that a considerable percentage of these are regular repeat visits from locals.

The communities which make up the bulk of the membership, have good access to the woodland and benefit directly from the project are the villages of High Spen, Rowland's Gill and Chopwell. The membership, however, includes interested people from across the UK and even overseas. The project is now providing excellent educational opportunities for local schools.

The core members of the group (15-20) have remained fairly constant from the outset and there are currently 8 local members regularly attending meetings. There has been close liaison with the British Trust for Conservation Volunteers (BTCV) throughout the life of the project.

The Group was formally constituted in the first year. The constitution is very simple and uncomplicated as befits a voluntary group with no formal or charitable status. Effectively it stipulates that the management committee should consist of no less than 12 persons (two of whom should be representatives from FE), that ordinary patrons are those paying an agreed amount annually and that people who have provided 'distinguished or outstanding service' to the woodland may become honorary patrons. There are approximately 250 ordinary patrons paying £3 per year and about 50 honorary patrons. The membership fee covers the production and mail-out of the tri-annual newsletter which provides information about events and projects, seeks comments and ideas and alerts the local community to FE work in the woodland.

The relationship between FOCW and FE is as follows: FOCW have monthly committee meetings which are normally attended by one or more FE officers. Decisions are made about projects on which FOCW funds will be spent. These projects are then approved by FE. If there is any major conflict, which seems unlikely, the FE District Manager would become involved.

The FE ranger often provides suggestions to FOCW about works which FE would like to see undertaken in the woodland but are unable to finance, and the committee decides whether to supply funding for these or not.

In a sense this appears to be the reverse of other rural development forestry situations, in so far as the community receives no material benefits from the management of the woodland, but devotes its energies to raising money for the woodland. The result of these efforts has been some employment and training for local people and significant educational facilities which are benefiting over 30 schools in the area.

What? The woodland sits on carboniferous strata with boulder clay, patches of sandy glacial deposits and a dramatic moraine ridge which rises to 200m above sea level.

Chopwell Wood occupies 384 hectares, part of a former extensive area of oak/hazel "wild wood" whose history is charted back at least as far as the 12th century. Oak was planted in the 19th century. The wood was drift under-mined in the 19th and early 20th century for coal deposits. A mineral rail-line ran through the wood.

Management was taken on by the Forestry Commission in 1919 from Armstrong College, now part of Newcastle University. Substantial fellings provided timber for the two wars and full restocking took place in 1952. The main species are European and Japanese larch, Corsican and Scots pine, Douglas fir and Sitka and Norway spruce. There is also an area of pre 1850 semi-natural oak woodland (a locally rare habitat) on the cliffs along the river Derwent, a mature birch woodland and other areas of broadleaves scattered through the woodland. FOCW manages a small area of birch/hazel/sycamore coppice from which they produce green wood for craftworkers.

FE has introduced a programme of small scale (1-2ha) felling and replanting coupes which add diversity and interest to the woodland. Large core areas are designated for either permanent cover or long term retention.

The woodland provides valuable habitat for red squirrels, great crested newts, wood ants, woodcock, brown long-eared bats and Daubenton's bats. There are also three WW2 bomb craters which have become ponds with significant ecological interest.

The woodland was designated a Woodland Park in 1994 and formally opened by David Bellamy. It has been given Site of Interest for Nature Conservation (SINC) status by Gateshead Borough Council.

Vision? The long term vision of FOCW is to work in partnership with FE in developing the wood for recreation, education and conservation and to encourage community responsibility for it. The aims of the group are to:

- promote and develop the visual amenity and recreational facilities of the wood
- encourage the use of the wood for recreational purposes
- develop conservation of wildlife, trees and plants
- improve security and safety for visitors
- reduce litter and vandalism
- promote community involvement in the management of the wood
- raise funds for use towards the aims of the organisation.

FE's management objectives give a greater priority to recreation and conservation than before, although timber production is still an objective. While it recognises that Chopwell Wood is a valuable landscape, recreational and ecological asset, FE also has the task of ensuring it is not a sink for public money

In 1993 the FOCW committee produced a 5 year 'development and management' plan. This contained proposals for the production of maps, leaflets, educational materials, a voluntary code of conduct; an honorary warden scheme, a quarterly newsletter and events programme, the creation of picnic areas and a resource/visitor centre. It also covered suggestions on the monitoring and control of conflicting uses (horses, bicycles etc), improvement of views, paths, entrances; car parking and litter control, and the creation of new wildlife ponds.

While a lot of effort and enthusiasm went into this, FOCW felt that once it had been finalised and presented to FE it was effectively 'shelved'. However they now recognise with hindsight that some of their ideas were probably more enthusiastic than practical, and in fact a lot of the proposals have, in the fullness of time, been implemented.

How? The project started with the production of the first newsletter in early 1992 and a schools competition to design a logo for the group. This was followed by the first fund raising event - a Christmas market held in the wood at the same time as the FE held its annual sale of Christmas trees. The main fundraising event is the annual sale of 5000 Christmas trees. This finances practically all of the FOCW activities. The sale was taken over by FOCW in 1993 and is now contracted out.

The other main event which is run for fun, publicity and education is the summer festival. This is a combination of an FE working woodland demonstration and FOCW stalls and events. Costs and responsibilities are shared by FC, FE and FOCW. It is likely that greater responsibility will be taken by FOCW in the future.

Smaller regular events include activities such as tree identification, fungal forays, teddy bears' picnics and orienteering. These are led by members of FOCW or FE.

The **milestones** have been:

1. The production of the FOCW development and management plan in 1993.
2. The appointment of a ranger in 1993 which demonstrated FE support for community involvement in Chopwell Wood.
3. Achievement of Woodland Park status in 1994 and the installation of a giant carved hands sculpture.
4. Creation of the woodland classroom in spring 1996.
5. FOCW provided input to the FE Forest Design Plan in 1996.
6. FE's invitation of the Royal Forestry Society to Chopwell and the use of the classroom for their annual meeting in May 1996.
7. Completion of the 1/2 mile nature trail and wildflower meadow in1997.
8. Meeting with FA in 1998, which FOCW felt was a turning point in the Forestry Commission's recognition of the role of FOCW.
9. Creation of the 'education pond' in 1999.
10. Pond restoration at the north end of the wood in January 2000.
11. Artist commissioned in Feb 2000 (with Arts Council support) to produce a second wood sculpture.

Once these capital works are complete they are owned by FE. Maintenance operates under an amicable agreement which currently works well for both parties.

Specification of FOCW funded projects is generally the responsibility of the FOCW committee. Implementation to date has either been by BTCV or FE. Supervision of the projects is generally undertaken by FE (often the ranger)- again this operates on a friendly, ad hoc basis. BTCV has been closely involved because of the connection on the FOCW committee and offers training opportunities for local people. FOCW is now considering the use of local contractors for some projects.

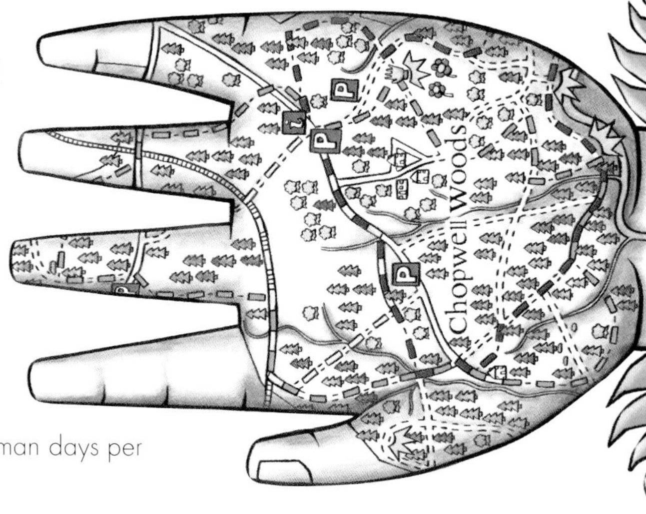

It has been estimated that BTCV work commissioned by FOCW has resulted in 200 man days per year in teams of 8 (which typically include 3 trainees, 1 supervisor and one special needs person). Trainees have not received certification, but involvement can provide units which contribute towards Forestry, Landscape or Ecology NVQs. Money paid by FOCW to FE has contributed a further 25 man days per year.

There is also a FOCW volunteer conservation group which has an annual programme of conservation tasks with training built in. Tasks include coppicing, small scale felling, marsh restoration, wildflower planting, bat box erection and pond management.

Probably the biggest **challenge** from the FOCW point of view was the initial unsatisfactory communication with FE and the difficulty in matching aims and agendas. Outwith committee meetings there hasn't been any formal mechanism for exchanging information. Both sides now feel they have a better understanding of each other's constraints and agendas although there is still a perception that while FOCW is obliged to tell FE of all its plans, it is not always kept fully informed of works being carried out by FE. This is apparently logistically difficult for FE. This has led to one or two disappointments for FOCW - for example the commissioning of an independent consultant to research and design 'a major water feature' which was then not taken forward. An earlier detailed discussion with FE could have avoided this problem.

One significant disappointment has been the failure of FOCW to establish a system of voluntary wardens. The original intention was to train enough volunteers to maintain a presence in the woodland every weekend. FOCW was keen to provide FOCW sweatshirts and badges. However, FE wasn't particularly happy about the idea of badged FOCW wardens and in the event there were insufficient volunteers for the scheme to be run.

Another disappointment which has caused FOCW considerable anguish is its red squirrel conservation programme. The group took the best advice available, but numbers of reds have diminished considerably, due mainly to disease and the advancing greys. FOCW has now managed to persuade FE to instigate a grey squirrel trapping programme and has provided further funding for this.

Greatest achievements? The main success has undoubtedly been the fundraising ability of FOCW. Since the early days it has never really been short of money - the problem has sometimes been to find appropriate ways of spending it.

The main achievements have been securing Woodland Park status, the creation of the forest classroom with its associated nature trail, meadow and pond and the involvement of so many schools.

Sources of help and advice? The group feels that it was very fortunate in incorporating people with a wide range of appropriate skills from the outset, in particular Iain Laidlaw's forestry knowledge. One of the core committee members was active in BTCV and had valuable conservation knowledge which proved to be of enormous benefit. Other skills have been in education and printing.

The main partners in the project are FOCW and FE and to a lesser extent FC. There has also been a close working relationship with BTCV. The only other organisation involved has been Gateshead Metropolitan Borough Council who own and manage the nearby Thornley Woods and Woodlands Centre. GMBC supplies skips, bin bags and wheelie bins for the annual 'Spring Clean' and Christmas litter clearance. It also donated some of the bulbs for planting around the car park.

The Tidy Britain group supplied information and litter pickers for the clean-ups and Northern Navigators have produced a map of the woodland and installed a permanent orienteering route. Help has also come from CPRE and from informal networking with existing community woodland groups such as the Borders Forest Trust.

FOCW has paid for local people to go on woodland craft training courses elsewhere- the offer of this opportunity was advertised in the local paper.

Future activities? In terms of the future, in many respects FOCW has achieved much of what it was originally set up to do- preservation and enhancement of the wood for the local community. While the changing climate in relation to community involvement in woodlands might make it possible for greater involvement and even 'ownership' of at least a part of the woodland by FOCW, the group seems content with the existing arrangement and understandably reluctant to commit the existing overworked volunteers to anything more demanding. Maybe FOCW has now reached its zenith- if it did finally fade away, it would leave a lasting legacy of community facilities which FE would continue to manage. However, it hopes to continue developing the woodland in partnership with FE into the indefinite future.

The main plans for the future are the creation of a tree identification trail, a sculpture trail to supplement the first sculpture put up in 1994, a booklet on the history of Chopwell Wood and a heritage trail. These features may be amalgamated on a single map or leaflet.

Ensuring continuity of active group members (i.e. the committee) has been a recent problem. While they have found that having a smaller active core has made for greater efficiency in meetings and implementing projects, they are now faced with the common problem of the organisation being kept alive by small number of overworked individuals. However, they have no doubt that the local communities are very much behind the project and all events are well attended and much enjoyed.

Lessons for others? The main lessons that FOCW feels it has learned are:

- the need for patience for the aims and objectives to turn into reality
- the need for good communication
- the ability to manage the enormous amounts of paperwork and endless discussions
- the importance of a formal committee structure
- the keeping of full accurate records

Contacts

Liz Searle
Membership Secretary
Friends of Chopwell Wood
2 Abert Street,
Rowlands Gill,
Tyne and Wear NE39 2JA
Website: www.jadz.demon.co.uk/focw

Cree Valley

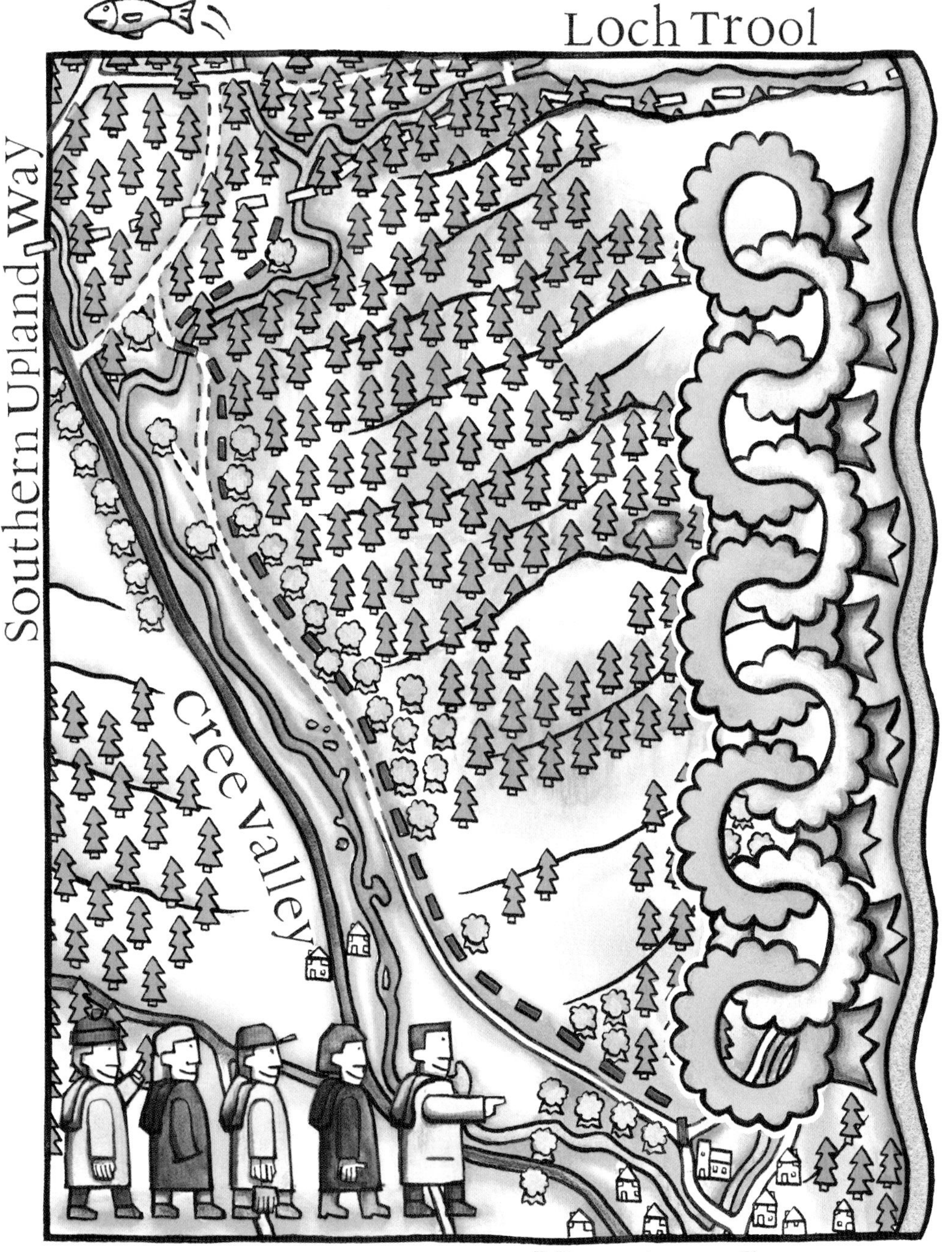

Summary

- The Cree Valley woodlands are located close to the River Cree and its tributaries, north of Newton Stewart in Galloway.
- The total area is 548 hectares in at least 10 identifiable areas. Species are mixed.
- Management is by agreement with the owners.
- Cree Valley Community Woodlands Trust runs the project.
- The Trust has charitable status.
- The key aim is to restore and link fragments of native woodlands.
- The project was conceived in 1996.

Cree Valley

Why? The original concept was biodiversity driven and emerged from the Forest Enterprise (FE) Environmental Panel in 1996. Because significant parts of the Cree, Minnoch and Trool catchments are owned by members of the Panel, notably FE and RSPB, the idea of linking woodlands together in the form of a Forest Habitat Network with great benefits for wildlife, began to develop. Through the increased biodiversity it is envisaged there will be improved opportunities for local people - to visit the improved woodlands and to develop opportunities for tourism, much needed in this part of Scotland.

Now that the Project Officer is in position, the local community is being brought together in support of the project. This applies particularly to the Town Woods next to Newton Stewart.

Who? The project is for the benefit of local people, particularly those residing within Newton Stewart and the Cree Valley. It is also for the benefit of the visiting public. The local economic benefits are perceived to be through tourism, local contracting jobs, training and education.

The community is hard to define precisely. In terms of influence over the project, the community is synonymous with the area covered by the Cree Valley Community Council. In terms of benefits, the community is considered to extend halfway to the next major centres, east and west- Castle Douglas and Stranraer. This includes Newton Stewart's 'feeder' villages. Local contractors would probably reside within 30 miles of the Cree Valley. Different aspects of the project define the local community slightly differently. At the same time, the project isn't parochial or exclusive and seeks to develop links with other initiatives in Scotland and beyond.

The core members of the Cree Valley Community Woodlands Trust are representatives of the partnership organisations- Cree Valley Community Council, Groundbase (Leader), Dumfries & Galloway Council, Forestry Commission, FE, RSPB, Freshfield Foundation, Scottish Natural Heritage (SNH), Newton Stewart Initiative, SEPA, West Galloway Fisheries Trust, Galloway Estates and Solway Heritage. It is hoped that the Town Woods will have community representatives in the future. From the perspective of FE and the other landowners, the project is a wonderful opportunity to develop links between the community and the forest. It is a vehicle which enables Government policies to be realised on the ground.

The group is structured as a Trust with charitable status with five Trustees elected by the membership. The Project Manager, Peter Hopkins, formerly the Principal Teacher in biology at the local High School, is answerable to the Trust. Supporting the Trustees is the wider Executive Group which includes the FE representative and any specialist advisors which the Trustees have identified. A larger Working Group is an ideas forum which is able to feed ideas and proposals through to the Trustees.

Phase 1 is a Millennium Forest for Scotland project, partially funded by MFST.

What? The Cree Valley Community Woodlands project encompasses at least ten identifiable areas of woodland, totalling 548 hectares, from Glenhead at the top of Glentrool to woodlands close to Newton Stewart, not far from where the Cree enters the Solway. What they have in common is an association with the river system. Several of the woods are oakwoods, designated as SSSIs; others are oakwoods underplanted with conifers, with the conifers due for removal. Part of the project involves clearing conifers back from the edge of the River Minnoch, a very significant salmon spawning area. Finally there are some opportunities for managing mixed species woodland and planting a few new areas. Not all of the woodlands are adjacent to each other, but as the project develops opportunities to influence the management of the gaps will increase.

Deer control, along with the scattered nature of the woodlands, poses a challenge for management. Access for management is not a problem.

The objectives of management will be different for each woodland depending upon the nature of the woodland and the owner's priorities. All subscribe to the overall aims of the project. The challenge will be to marry these different plans together to form a coherent whole.

Vision? The feasibility study written by Phil Ratcliffe of Bidwells discusses the vision of the project in some detail. In it, he suggests:

"...a mosaic of non-native and native woodland interspersed with moorland, grassland and wetland. The commercial benefits of forestry based on non-native species will continue as a dominant part of the economy, but its visual and biological impact, particularly in the upper parts of the river and its tributaries, will be ameliorated by replacing many road and riverside conifers with native broadleaves." He goes on to suggest that local people will have a significant role in developing and shaping the strategic application of the vision and in the actual delivery.

The **objectives** for the project are:

- To create a native broadleaved community woodland of national importance... through a community partnership... improving the social, ecological and economic value of the Cree Valley.
- To restore and link existing fragments of native woodlands and associated habitats... creating opportunities for species of high conservation value to colonise from existing ancient woodlands.
- To promote the enhancement, interpretation and conservation of biodiversity, landscape, archaeological and cultural aspects of the built heritage.
- To extend public access by exploring and developing the potential for new routes, particularly linking to the Southern Upland Way.
- To enhance the fishery by improving aquatic and riparian management.
- To stimulate local economic activity... supporting tourism and cottage industries which can utilise native broadleaves.

- To develop an interpretative strategy to encompass the whole of the Cree Valley catchment... develop existing visitor facilities to the highest standards and provide new recreational opportunities...

How? Once the members of the FE Environmental Panel embraced the concept of linking the woodlands to form a catchment approach, a forestry consultant, Peter Ross, was contracted to develop the project and make contact with all interested parties including the landowners. The Trust doesn't own any land and works through 25 year management agreements with the owners.

The **milestones** have been:

1. The meeting of the FE Environmental Panel in 1996.
2. The development of support from interested parties during 1996 and 1997.
3. The commitment of funding from the Freshfield Foundation in early 1998.
4. The establishment of a tree nursery in Penninghame Prison in autumn 1998.
5. The formation of the Trust in December 1998.
6. The Feasibility Study was completed in January 1999.
7. MFS funding was confirmed in February 1999.
8. Public access improvements at Wood of Cree in June 1999.
9. Peter Hopkins began working voluntarily in July and officially in August 1999.

The biggest **challenges** have been:

- The funding for the Project Officer. Whereas the representatives of the partners and the forestry consultant have been able to get the project off the ground, the management of the project has been dependent upon having the full-time Project Officer in post. Other targets have been missed due to the delay in appointing the PO and this has caused problems with the funders. MFST, in particular, has been unrealistic and inflexible with the scheduling of targets. The **solution** has been to get the PO into post as quickly as possible with Peter Hopkins working voluntarily for six weeks in order to allow the project to go ahead. Now it is a question of re-prioritising the targets and trying to catch up on the key ones.
- Dealing with matched funding. Some sources of funding, such as Rural Challenge, didn't come through. Others, such as the Forestry Partnership Programme, only came through at the last moment after additional lobbying. Some stated sources of funding were, with hindsight, wishful thinking and weren't secure. Another problem was that the development costs ran well over budget, causing knock-on effects. Timber sales have formed part of the package and this has been hit by the drop in prices. The **solution** has been, and continues

to be, to revisit the original funding sources, repackaging the project as appropriate, resubmitting applications and seeking out new sources of funding.

- The sheer administrative burden. Dealing with the requirements of many organisations and owners has been a huge effort. The **solution** is persistence. The major aspects of the bureaucracy are now under control, but it will continue to absorb a large proportion of the PO's workload keeping on top of it.

Greatest achievements? Developing a good working relationship between all of the partners and funders is seen to be the greatest achievement to date and the biggest challenge. As the project develops, there is a perceptible increase in confidence amongst the partners that it can be delivered to a very high standard. There is a strong degree of support coming from the top of several of the key partner organisations.

What is most challenging for the future is trying to assess what is realistic from amongst the plethora of ideas emanating from the partners, funders and, increasingly in the future, the community. Trying to meet deadlines and partner requirements will continue to be challenging. On the management side, much of the proposed work is going ahead without adequate baseline surveys being in place. It will be difficult, in the future, to know how successful the project has been.

Sources of help and advice? With such a large group of partners, most of the required skills in areas such as woodland management, riparian management, fundraising and education are to be found within the group, one advantage of the partnership approach. The downside is that the wider range of skills to be found in the community are not yet adequately available. These will include dealing with tourists, developing recreational activities, small scale working with woodland products, wildlife observation, etc. To date the input of skills from outside the core group has been minimal.

All of the partners and funders have been very supportive, sharing knowledge and devoting time to the project. Forest Enterprise, in particular, has been very positive and committed to the project.

The principal funders, including those with in kind contributions are Freshfield Foundation, Millennium Forest for Scotland, Dumfries & Galloway Council, Groundbase, SNH, Forestry Commission and Forest Enterprise. The difficulty in raising matched funds has already been described.

The only training to date has been a group of local unemployed young people. They were trained in path making, through the Scottish Wildlife Trust.

Future activities? The MFST project forms Phase 1 of the CVCW project. The outputs for this include 62 hectares of conifer removal, 61 hectares of native woodland planting, 49 hectares of regeneration, 22 hectares of oakwood thinning, nine kilometres of new fencing, four kilometres of new footpaths, three kilometres of footpath improvements, two car parks, four

interpretation panels, two festivals or training events, leaflet production, the setting up of a CVCW membership organisation and a timber marketing initiative. In addition to all of this, the PO is currently working with community groups, schools, the prison, local unemployed, people with disabilities, youth groups and is developing a supporters group for the Town Woods.

The project is long-term. Phase 1 is expected to last approximately two years. The management agreements run out after 25 years and can be extended. It is anticipated that the project will become embedded into the local community and expand into adjacent and similar areas. Already, the owner of a significant area between two project woods has entered into a large scale planting programme with design input from the project. There is no exit strategy as the partners believe strongly in the project. Funding is, as usual, precarious. As the profile of the project rises and a quality product is delivered, funding should become easier.

It is hard to say where the project will level out in terms of its activity. It will be greater than Phase1. The signs are that there are many people in the community who can relate to the project's objectives and who will support it in some form or another. Already there are several add-on projects and with increasing community involvement, this is likely to increase. The project could be very significant.

Keeping the core group going isn't a problem as most are representatives or are there because of vested interests. Diversifying it to become more representative of the local community is a challenge. The secret is to ensure that it is seen to be achieving results and that it is enjoyable to be involved with.

Lessons for others? The main lesson is to ensure that the financial package is secure and in place. If it isn't, it affects people's lives. For any project the key ingredients are trust and confidence. When asked how close the project was to delivering the ideal community woodland, the answer was 30%. The seeds have been sown and are starting to germinate.

Contacts

Dr Peter Hopkins
Project Manager

Cree Valley Community
Woodlands Trust

Daltamie, Palnure
Newton Stewart DG8 7BE

Email: peter.hopkins@cvcwt.org.uk

Culag

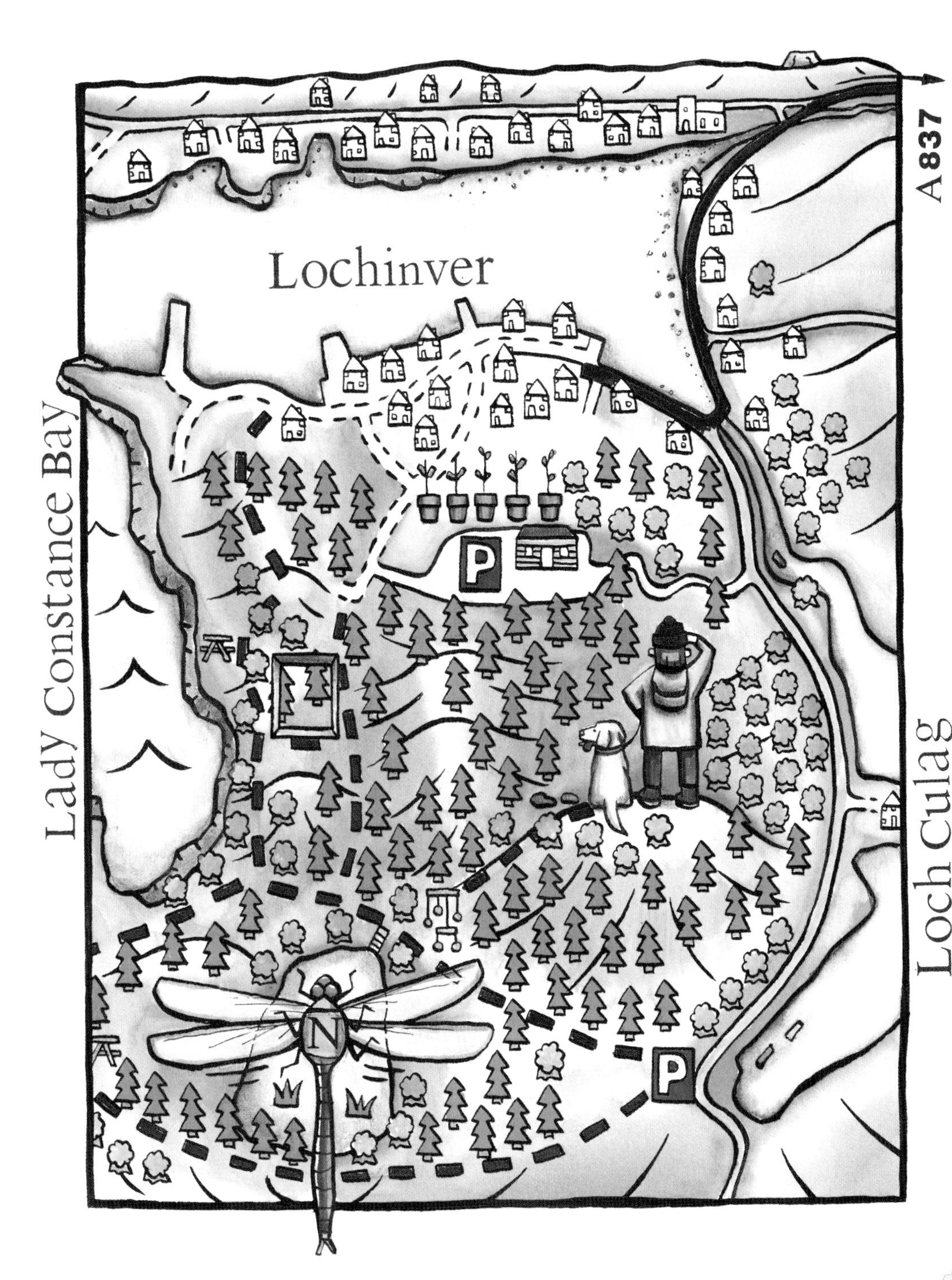

Summary

- Culag Wood is situated adjacent to Lochinver, Sutherland in the north-west of Scotland.
- The wood consists of 36 hectares of mixed conifer plantation with pockets of broadleaves.
- The woodland is managed under a 50 year lease from the local estate.
- Culag Community Woodland Trust runs the project.
- CCWT is a company limited by guarantee with charitable status.
- The key aim is to optimise the local benefits from the wood.
- The project was initiated in 1992.

Culag

Why? Assynt Estates owned Culag Wood before the Culag Community Woodland Trust (CCWT) took it over. The management of the wood had been neglected and it had begun to look uncared for. Situated right beside the village, the wood is clearly visible from Lochinver and its current state was detracting from the scenic value of the area. Members of the Assynt Community Council began to think that the local community could manage the wood for its own benefit and in 1992 the community council approached Assynt Estates and Highland Regional Council (HRC), who owned a small corner of the wood, with a view to obtaining a lease.

It was believed that most of the necessary skills required to manage the wood were already in the parish and that there was enough enthusiasm to carry the project forward. Additional funds for managing the woods could be available to a community group where they would not be to a private estate. A 50 year lease with an option for a further 50 was signed with Assynt Estates in January 1996, although work had started well before that through an informal agreement.

Who? CCWT exists for the benefit of the local people in the parish of Assynt, Sutherland and for all the visitors to the area. Lochinver is the biggest centre of population, but the parish stretches from Kylesku to Elphin and Culkein Stoer to Inverkirkaig and members come from all over the parish with a few from further afield in Scotland. CCWT is a company limited by guarantee and a registered charity. There are eight member directors and four appointed directors including the local countryside ranger and councillor, the factor from Assynt Estates and the chairman of Assynt Community Council. The group is supported by the local area officer from SNH and Jon Priddy of the North Highland Forest Trust (NHFT), both of whom regularly attend directors' meetings. There are about 60 members at present.

Local people have developed skills such as timber harvesting and footpath construction in the woods and gone on to apply them elsewhere, thereby contributing to the local economy.

The local primary school uses the woodland and has been involved in the recent treeplanting activities. The playgroup uses it in conjunction with the Ranger Service. The Wildlife Watch Group (Scottish Wildlife Trust) has a small tree nursery next to the main car park and plans to be involved with the proposed woodland work, including the growing on of aspen root cuttings. Many people walk their dogs in the woods.

What? The wood consists of 36 hectares of mixed conifer plantation (larch, Douglas fir, Norway spruce, Sitka spruce and Scots pine) with pockets of native broadleaves (downy birch, rowan, aspen, oak, hazel, alder, holly and willow). A few other non-native broadleaves are present such as sycamore and beech. It was originally planted in 1847 but was almost entirely clearfelled and replanted in the mid 1930s. A few mature conifers survive from the original planting. The wood has essentially been unmanaged since the time of the 1930s plantings.

The original paths had become overgrown and blocked with fallen trees. There is now a network of well made paths with new ones being created and others maintained. In the centre of the wood there is a bog which was a small loch before being drained in 1847. This adds greatly to the diversity of habitats within the wood and has a small walkway out to its edge. Birch and spruce are regenerating slowly on the bog (which has a little open water - great for dragonflies) and this causes a management problem or a management delight depending on your point of view.

The wood was fenced against deer in 1996 in conjunction with the Community Council which was ring fencing the whole of Lochinver. All species of trees are regenerating despite the best efforts of several red and roe deer which seem to have both a pass key and the better of the local stalker!

CCWT started out with a view to optimising the local benefits from the wood and this ideal remains unchanged today. The following management objectives are taken from the new community produced management plan:

1. To manage the silviculture in a sustainable way.
2. To conserve and enhance the nature conservation of the wood.
3. To encourage access and use of the woods for enjoyment and recreation, towards fostering love, understanding and respect for the woods and the natural environment in general.
4. To provide opportunities to acquire skills and employment in forestry and related activities.
5. To share our experience and resources and to learn from others the processes involved in community forestry.
6. To maintain and organise administration.

Vision? It is hoped that the maximum number of people can enjoy and benefit from what is a precious resource in this part of Scotland. While community groups are always extremely grateful for grants, CCWT is looking forward to the day when it can become self-funding for the majority of its projects and be in a position to help other local groups, practically and financially. It will have to somehow become expert at small scale timber extraction and would be willing to be part of a machinery ring in the north of Scotland. Perhaps in the future CCWT will be in a position to manage more forest land.

CCWT also envisages individuals or small groups using the resources of the woods to develop small businesses and will be there to help provide the necessary training and encouragement.

How? After Assynt Estates and HRC had agreed to the lease in principle, HRC funded a consultant's report which was completed early in 1994. A public meeting of interested residents was called and a Steering Group elected. Meanwhile through an informal agreement, work had started on improving the footpaths funded by HRC, Caithness and Sutherland Enterprise (CASE), and SNH. The lease with Assynt Estates was signed in 1996.

The first major task was the organising of the felling of six hectares of the wood which had recently succumbed to windthrow, and the sale of the timber produced. For this to happen a road fit to take large timber wagons had to be constructed from scratch. As a first project this was rather intimidating, but urgently needed to be done to clear up the "mess" and provide funds for future projects. The road was built in 1997 and extraction took place in 1998. This road is now the main access road for the public.

In 1996 CCWT became part of the Millennium Forest for Scotland (MFST) group of projects. Management took place supported by a Woodland Improvement Grant (WIG) during 1997-99, organised with the help of Jon Priddy of the then North West Sutherland Native Woodland Project.

Part of the WIG project was the setting up of an interpretative trail called the "All the Time in the World Trail" which consists of a dozen pieces of artwork located in amongst the trees designed to inspire and add to the woodland experience. There is also the nature trail (to be renewed in 2000/01) and an orientreeing course (spelt correctly).

Greatest achievements? The greatest achievement to date has probably been organising the clearfell and timber sale of the windblown area.

The greatest challenge for CCWT, which fell mostly upon the secretary John Gibson, was dealing with all the paper work, especially that generated by MFST, which is still ongoing. MFST's system was so confusing that when the new secretary took over in November 1998 she eventually had to get a representative from MFST to come up to Lochinver and sort it all out for herself (which she did admirably). The confusion was over which projects were in the WIG, which in MFST's contract and which were otherwise funded. It came down to different sections of particular paths - nightmarish!

Sources of help and advice? Members have wide ranging useful skills. Several trained in footpath work in Culag Wood and there is now a resident footpath team. There are two rangers and other members of the Assynt Field Club amongst the membership. There are joiners, engineers, half a dozen chainsaw operators (trained in Culag Community Woodland), artists, sculptors, tipi-builders and many more who love to be active in the woods.

In the early days funding was received from HRC, CASE and SNH, with additional help from ACE- HI. The group more importantly had the backing of the local community and estates. Two local contractor/consultants Bernard Planterose and Martin Howard produced the first management plan and were a huge help with practical advice. Since those early days, SNH and CASE continue to fund projects and training courses and representatives attend most directors' meetings. Jon Priddy of NHFT has been extremely supportive and helpful and is always willing to travel over to advise or demonstrate woodland management skills. He organised a demonstration day for small forestry machinery which was attended by people from all over the far north of Scotland.

Future activities? There are regular firewood days on the first Saturday of each month during the winter and usually some sort of fun day on the second Saturday of each month. A mushroom-log demonstration day was held in February 2000 to attract a different sort of member: those who are not so able to be active in flinging timber about. A mountain bike trail for the 10 – 16 year old age group is being planned together with some further footpath construction to complete the network. A timber hut is being built in the main car park as a base for operations and for shelter. The group is currently looking into the possibility of having a part-time project officer to co-ordinate all the projects.

The group believes that it is important to have something for all age groups in the woods. There seems to be no shortage of ideas and projects but they nearly all come from the directors. There is a need to get the message across that if anyone at all wants to develop a project in the wood they can. There needs to be a balance of creative projects and fun days. In 1999, a theatre group performed a play throughout the woods with the active participation of the young audience- a truly wonderful day. CCWT would like to encourage other groups to use the wood and is circulating information about Culag Wood to colleges to encourage biological survey work.

Lessons for others? Sometimes the group feels as though little is happening, but as with other small voluntary organisations there is only so much time busy individuals can give. It would be better if the organisation of particular projects could be delegated to members other than the directors. There is a need to keep the public well informed so that they can feel part of what is happening, a newsletter is a possibility.

The best advice is that if you are stuck, ASK SOMEONE. Don't struggle and worry - it just wears you out. CCWT would like to network more with other community woods and there is an open invitation to any group out there who would like to visit the Culag Wood anytime.

Contacts

Claire Belshaw
Secretary

Culag Community Woodland Trust
Caladh, Stoer
Sutherland IV27 4JE

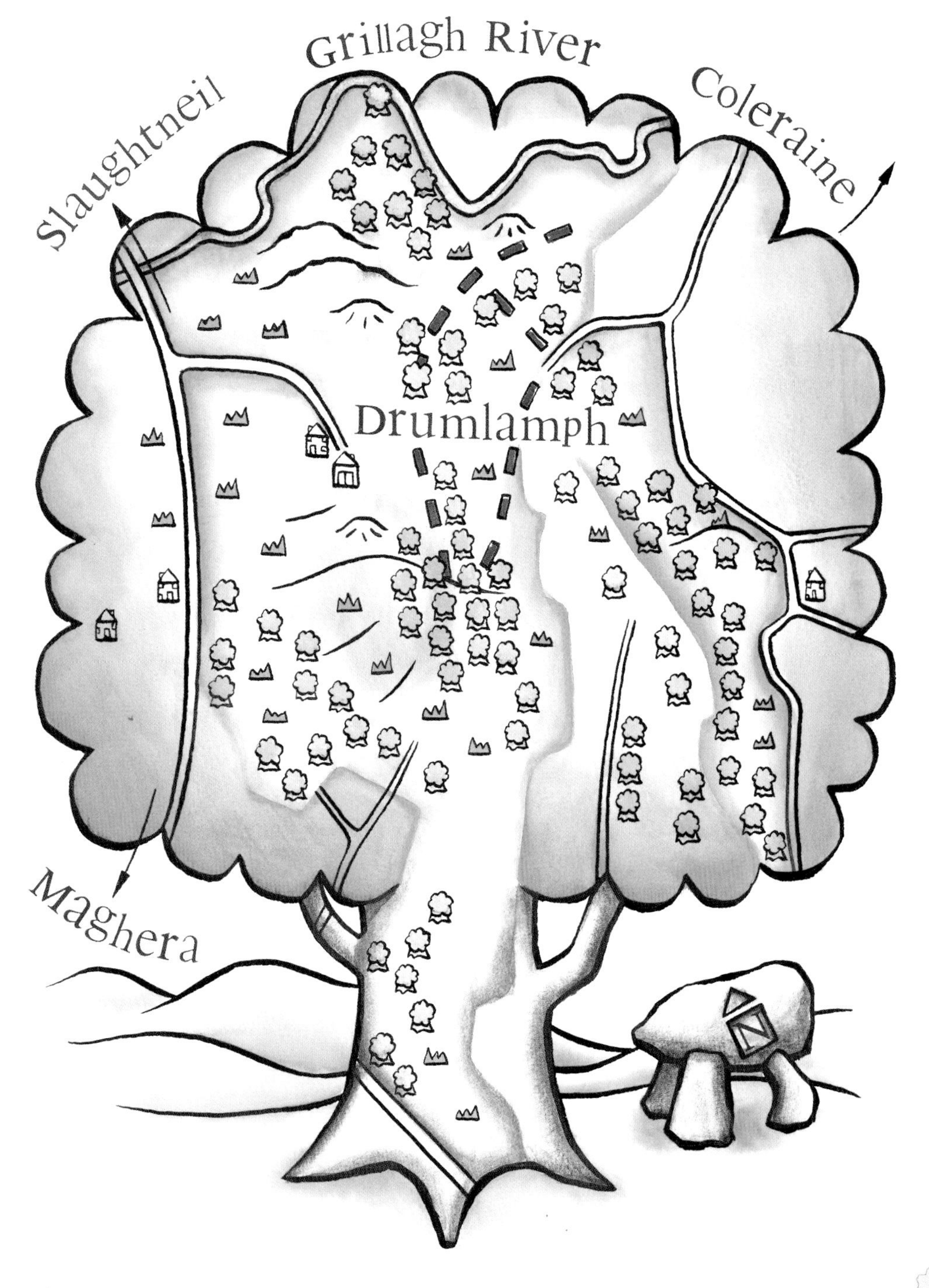

Summary

- Drumlamph is in mid Ulster, to the east of the Sperrin Hills.
- The core ancient woodland area (oak, hazel and associated species) is 19 hectares surrounded by over 300 hectares of associated habitats, including scrub, raised bog and grassland.
- The wood is managed on a 999 year lease between the Woodland Trust and the individual owners.
- Carntogher Community Association runs the project.
- The Association is a company limited by guarantee with charitable status.
- The key aims are to preserve and enhance the fabric and character of the rural community.
- The woodland project began in 1998.

Drumlamph

Why? The Carntogher Community Association (CCA) was formed in 1992 to preserve and enhance the fabric and character of the rural community in the general Carntogher area of south Derry (two miles north of Maghera). Its plans, already partially realised, include an Irish language playgroup, light industry, community meeting rooms and office space, a multi-media suite, a cultural festival and hill-walking trails. An area of ancient woodland and associated habitats at the core of Carntogher, known as Drumlamph (the ridge of the wild garlic), was identified as having potential in the economic and cultural regeneration of the area.

The CCA was already up and running when the idea of managing Drumlamph for the benefit of the local community was first mooted. This has enabled progress to be made relatively quickly.

Who? The project is for the benefit primarily of the people who live in the 14 or 15 townlands lying below Carntogher Mountain, an eastern outlier of the Sperrins. The area is fairly well defined by the mountain and the main roads. It is a rural area with around 300 households and 1500 people. There has been a lack of community facilities although a new primary school was opened in 1997. The population profile is characterised by a high proportion of young people (42% under 19) and many old people with fewer in between. This is related to the high unemployment levels (21%) and this, in turn, is the reason for the CCA's existence.

The CCA is a company limited by guarantee with charitable status. There are 14-16 Directors who are elected at the AGM. Small sub-committees with separate bank accounts are set up to deal with specific projects such as Drumlamph. There are 3 Directors on this group plus co-opted members such as the representatives of involved organisations. It is the CCA which will employ the project manager when that person is selected. There has been no need for a public meeting to initiate the project. The interest was already there and has been slowly growing. Constant feedback is given through close community links in such a rural area.

What? The core area of ancient semi-natural mixed deciduous woodland extends to 19 hectares (50 acres) and is surrounded by roughly 300 hectares (750 acres) of associated habitats- hawthorn/birch scrub, cut-over bog, marshy grassland, unimproved acid grassland, acid mire, new woodland, hedges and open water. The whole area was wooded at the time of the earliest maps, in 1609, although the plantation period in the 17th and 18th centuries saw massive cutting of the oakwood for shipbuilding and Derry's walls.

One third of the total area has been surveyed and evaluated for its nature conservation value. It scores highly in terms of diversity, rarity, naturalness, fragility, ecological position, potential value and intrinsic appeal. The core woodland area scores even more highly. Botanical surveys have shown the wood/mire area to contain a rich diversity of flora and fauna with 12 primary indicator plants having been identified so far. Very few introduced or naturalised species are found in the wood.

Of particular note are the diverse bryophyte community and the presence of the uncommon red squirrel and Irish hare. Important bird species present are the long eared owl, buzzard, peregrine falcon, sparrowhawk, grasshopper warbler and redstart.

The ancient woodland area is fairly open (60% canopy cover) and dominated by sessile oak and common alder with elm, birch, hazel, holly and hawthorn also featuring. Height ranges from 4 to 14 metres. It has been unmanaged for a long period of time and has been heavily grazed to the detriment of its species diversity. The scattered scrub is dominated by silver birch, hawthorn and whins. The cut-over bog has scattered downy birch, common alder and goat willow.

The proposed management for the ancient woodland is to exclude stock with new fencing, coppice the hazel, plant a small number of sessile oak, protect natural regeneration, retain all dead wood and manage 20% of the area on a non-intervention basis. The 23 hectares of birch scrub is to be managed by excluding stock, controlling bracken, planting sessile oak, retaining dead wood and cutting back 'leggy' scrub. The intention on the cut-over bog is to restore the bog and remove the encroaching trees. In addition, 13 hectares of adjoining land are to be planted as a new native woodland.

Overall the objectives for the site are:

- to protect and enhance habitats, linking existing sites of conservation value
- to restore and restructure ancient woodland through planned management, making a contribution to the delivery of the UK and local Biodiversity Action Plans
- to provide access for quiet informal recreation
- to enhance the community aspects with guided walks and local participation

Vision? The long-term vision for the project is to bring the woodland and other habitats back into a healthy condition. The oak woodland of Carntogher shown on the ancient maps, survived until comparatively recent times and forms part of the history and culture of this part of mid Ulster. Indeed, the symbol of the county is the oak (Derry means oakwood). It is believed that local people feel good about the landscape being looked after and it will contribute to the growing feeling of self-confidence.

There are many objectives for the project, intertwined with the overall objectives of the CCA. These are:

1. The supporting of local jobs through the management activities.
2. The development of tourism related jobs, both directly, in the form of guiding, and indirectly e.g. bed nights.
3. The development of environmental education through an on-site classroom, hides, bird and bat boxes and interpretation panels.

4. The provision of informal access.
5. The production and processing of hardwood timber from the new woodlands in the form of coppice materials, charcoal, rustic furniture and ash hurling sticks.

The protection and restoration of the various habitats is the primary objective.

How? The project began as an off-shoot of the CCA's rural regeneration policy. The structure was already in place with a tight administrative structure. This impressed potential supporting organisations such as the Woodland Trust and the Dept of Environment as well as funders such as the HLF.

Agriculture is in a poor way and with an ageing farming population, alternative ways of managing the land are on the agenda. Since the initial group of owners signed 999 year leases to give up control of their land in exchange for up front compensation, there has been a flurry of interest from adjoining landowners. It is hoped that the area of the project will expand in the future. Local people used to visit the woodland more often in the past than of late and there was feeling that it had become more inaccessible through flooding of the wetland and tracks.

The **milestones** have been:

1. Carntogher Community Association was set up in January 1992.
2. A full time Gaelic Athletic Association youth officer was in post for 3 years and stimulated youth activity and confidence.
3. A new state of the art primary school was opened in September 1996 and has 120 pupils. The local Irish language school will form a unit within the school in 2001.
4. Discussions with the Heritage Lottery Fund (HLF) and the Woodland Trust (WT) were initiated in September 1998.
5. Discussions with landowners took place in December 1998.
6. Discussions with the Dept of Environment (DoE) began in early 1999.
7. Also early in 1999, the Moyola Valley Development Partnership provided funding for an environmental audit.
8. The environmental audit was carried out by a local ecologist and accepted in April 1999.
9. The HLF application was finally completed in June 1999
10. Funding was confirmed in August 1999.
11. Contracts were signed between the Woodland Trust and the landowners in January 2000.

Some **challenges** have emerged as a result of bureaucracy, but this has gone fairly smoothly due to the experience of the group members in completing forms. The HLF had to appoint someone in Northern Ireland before the application could be submitted. The HLF sent out two forms and the group filled in the wrong one, so the application had to be resubmitted. The **solution** is to stay calm and build experience.

Greatest achievements? Obtaining HLF funding to purchase the land has been the highlight. The complementary relationship between CCA and WT was commented upon. The WT's experience in woodland management and access to funding has been of great help to the CCA with its personal contacts with the landowners and other interested local people.

Sources of help and advice? The skills found within the group are impressive:

- Personal networking and knowledge of how local people think
- Knowledge of funding mechanisms and funding bodies
- A good working relationship with the main players
- Knowledge of the culture and history of the area
- Financial appraisal
- Administration. Already the group has a tight administrative structure with computerised systems, well organised accounts and a part-time secretary

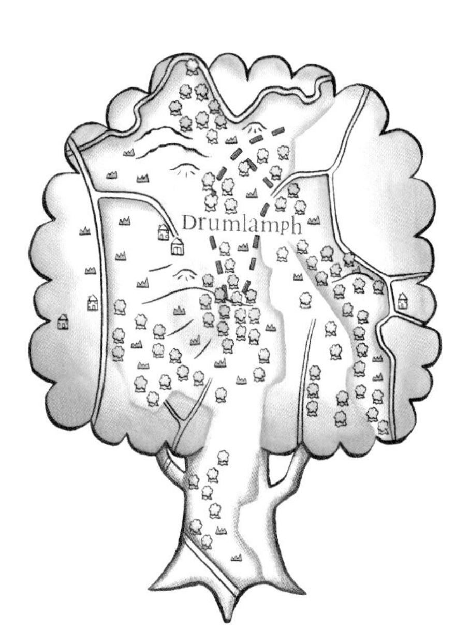

The group does recognise its limitations and brought in the following skills from outside:

- Ecological survey and management planning from the environmental consultant
- Funding application and credibility from the Woodland Trust
- Land conveyancing from a local solicitor
- Group structure design to set up CCA from the NI Community Development Association

CCA has found WT to be a sympathetic organisation to work with. WT did the first HLF application. HLF was apologetic and helpful after its mistake over the forms. The tone of DoE was cool at first when it was pointed out that its audit of significant woods had missed out Drumlamph. However, it soon warmed up and since then their managers and surveyors have been supportive and approved substantial funding. The Environment and Heritage section is understaffed and feeling the pressure of cutbacks. The main funders to date have been HLF and DoE. There has been no training of local people in practical or management skills.

Future activities? The project will probably grow as other owners make land available, assuming that additional funds can be obtained. The WT is interested in further acquisitions in partnership with CCA and other bodies such as the wildlife trust. This will link the core areas to the wider agricultural landscape and up onto the mountain, developing a habitat network and opportunities for walking routes. There are other funding opportunities including strong Ulster/American links, possibly via the www.

How quickly the project grows depends both on the funding situation and the project officer/management team. Awareness of the project will spread beyond Carntogher and involvement by schools, groups and individuals could broaden out to the whole of mid Ulster. Success breeds success and business opportunities could develop from the project. Once people's livelihoods depend to some extent upon the project, its sustainability in the longer term is almost guaranteed.

Lessons for others?

- Talk to everybody you can
- Decide what you want to do
- Temper that with what can be done

The original intention was to implement the complete project themselves. They then realised that the WT is set up to buy and manage woodland and it made sense to use its skill, knowledge and credibility. So there are other lessons:-

- Share out areas of the project where you can, you lose some of the ownership and control but you also lose some of the workload and liabilities
- Joint ownership equals joint liabilities (everybody needs to sleep well at night)

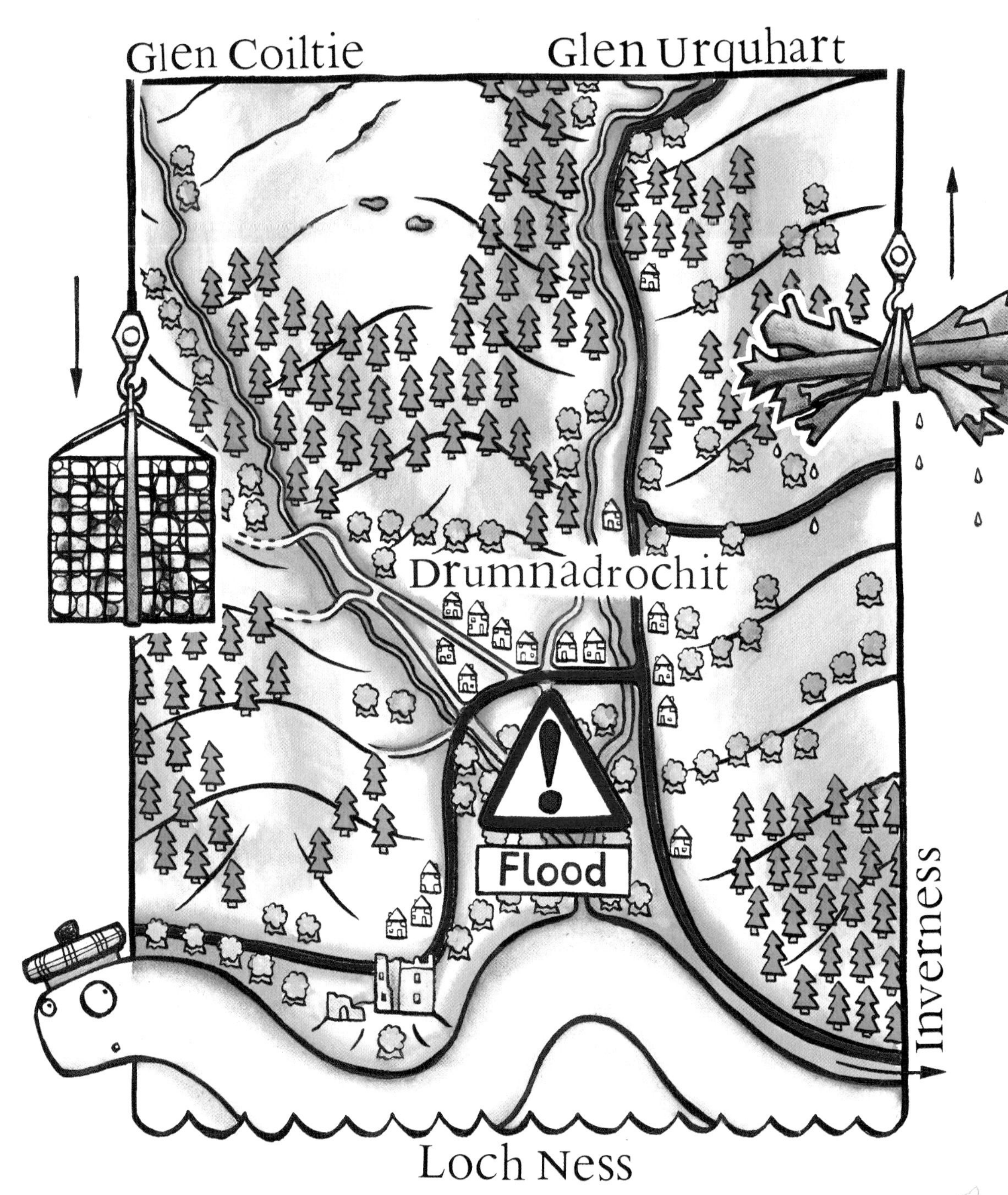

Summary

- Glen Urquhart runs westwards from Drumnadrochit on Loch Ness.
- One third of the glen is under trees, of which the majority are conifers.
- The management of the glen's forests and woodlands is influenced by the project.
- Glen Urquhart Land Use Partnership is a partnership between the Community Council and Forest Enterprise.
- The management group is a sub-committee of the Community Council.
- The key aim is sustainable land management for the entire catchment, leading to healthy fish populations and reduced flooding.
- The group was formed in October 1997.

Glen Urquhart

Why? There had been severe flooding in the village of Drumnadrochit, perhaps three times in ten years. Many homes and premises associated with the tourist trade had been affected. It was easy to look upstream and blame the forestry. The fact was that the rivers Enrick and Coillte were classic spate rivers and the village had been built in the danger zone. The community decided that steps had to be taken to alleviate the situation in as far as that was possible. The Glen Urquhart Community Council called a public meeting to discuss the problem and a sub-committee, consisting of five people, three of them riparian owners, was set up to explore the issue further and to take some action. The remit was to 'find ways to manage the river'.

The group started with a narrow focus on the riparian zone but soon realised that land use activities away from the rivers, such as drainage and tree felling, were also having a considerable effect on the rivers. Consequently the focus widened to include the whole catchment. The health of the fish population and the water flow characteristics are taken to be indicative of the health of the whole glen. The catchment approach has been very effective.

Who? The project is for the benefit of the people who live and work in the glen, and indirectly for the many visitors. This community is largely the same as the Community Council (CC) electorate with the largest population centre being Drumnadrochit. The people who live in the glen work mainly in the tourist and service sectors. Many commute to Inverness and few work in agriculture or forestry these days. The CC has good support from the local community but, as usual, few attend its meetings.

The management group is still a sub-committee of the CC but has evolved into a partnership with Forest Enterprise (FE) and is now known as the Glen Urquhart Land Use Partnership. The link to the CC is seen to be very helpful in giving the group a democratic mandate and also confers practical benefits, such as using the Highland Council tendering system. The original five volunteers still form the group and include three riparian owners, the former CC chair and the local councillor. As well as the formal relationship with FE, good working relationships have been developed with other organisations such as SNH, SEPA and the Ness District Fisheries Board (which one of the group chairs). All the owners in the catchment have been contacted. As well as FE, there are a few private forests managed by forest companies, private estates, farms and crofts. Most have been supportive of the initiative.

What? 33% of the catchment is forest (of which 15% belongs to Forest Enterprise), 15% farmland and the rest is open hill. The species balance for the whole of the Fort Augustus District is Sitka spruce 35%, Lodgepole pine 27%, Scots pine 17%, other conifers 13%, broadleaves 8%. As the second rotation kicks in, the proportion of Lodgepole pine will decrease with increases in Sitka spruce and broadleaves. The other species will remain about the same. In the FE plantations in Glen Urquhart, this process is already well under way and little of the first rotation is left (mostly as long term retentions). The private forests tend to be much younger and are probably less diverse. There are also substantial areas of semi-natural woodland on some of the estates and farms. The rivers themselves have very diverse riparian woodland, especially on the lower reaches. These woodlands are a concern as they haven't been actively managed in the past and natural regeneration is being prevented by heavy grazing.

Most of the FE forest has been through a restructuring process, based mainly on landscape considerations, but with some benefits to the ecology. The age structure has widened from the narrow range of the first rotation. Together with the private forests in the glen there is now a good range of tree ages, but really mature trees are under-represented. There are few constraints to management. The types of forest in the glen are diverse, from semi-natural birch and riparian woodland to purely commercial plantations, with much in between of a multi-benefit nature. The objectives for the various blocks will vary accordingly.

Vision? The vision for the project is sustainable land management within the catchment. This takes in natural woodland, a diverse ecology, a stable river system and increasing fish populations. Both of the rivers provide important nursery areas. Local employment and supporting the local economy are major concerns of the Community Council. The vision has been summarised as ensuring that the glen stays beautiful and habitable, and the village isn't damaged by flooding.

How? The project started with a public meeting in October 1997 called by the Glen Urquhart Community Council to which Forest Enterprise and other riparian owners were invited. At this meeting, five local people with some knowledge and interest in this matter were appointed to a sub-committee. The CC owns no land, but seeks to influence the management of all the land in the catchment, particularly that which is covered with trees. As representatives of the community, the Glen Urquhart Land Use Partnership has found that most owners are very willing to comply with the project's aims and advice.

The **milestones** have been:

1. The formation of the group in October 1997.
2. A site meeting with Forest Enterprise in January 1998.
3. A presentation by the Forestry Commission's hydrologist, Tom Nisbet, to explain forest hydrology in February 1998.
4. Survey of the majority of the river with a photographic record by February 1998.
5. All known riparian owners written to by February 1998.
6. Considerable amounts of timber removed from the river by FE and other riparian owners.

7. Repairs made to river banks and excess gravel removed from a major site by September 1998.
8. Good working relationship developed between the partners and associated organisations and individuals.
9. A flood warning system has been developed and is currently being implemented.

The Partnership facilitates action by encouraging owners, finding funds to help pay for the work and obtaining permissions, for example for the extraction of gravel from the river. It has decided to put the emphasis on action rather than on commissioning expensive consultants' reports.

The work has been divided up into three phases:

1. Short-term. Survey of the river to determine areas where prompt action is required to clear debris such as fallen tree roots in order to reduce the risk of log jams in the event of spate floods.
2. Medium-term. Establishment of a basic management system for the river and tackling of some of the more serious erosion problems which exist.
3. Long-term. Establishment of a viable and ongoing system to monitor the river and its catchment, ensuring that steps are taken to minimise damage to the environment (with all that that term implies), bearing in mind that the two rivers are natural spate rivers.

This work will largely be carried out by local businesses and individuals so there will be some economic benefits to the local community.

The biggest **challenges** were (and continue to be):

- Obtaining funding, especially the chore of form filling. The solution is to get on and do it but the **suggestion** was made that this could be a service provided by a support person should a Community Woodland Association come into existence. Fundraising tends to be a seasonal activity, best suited to the winter when tourist related activities are at a lower level. Unfortunately, this doesn't always coincide with funding deadlines.
- Apathy in the local community. The same people do things, but most express a willingness to help. The **solution** is to keep everybody informed of progress with regular updates.

Greatest achievements? The greatest achievement has been getting almost all of the individual riparian owners working for the good of all and for the benefit of the local community. The partnership with Forest Enterprise has become very positive. It is now clear that this concerted effort is likely to achieve the project's objectives of reduced floods and improved fish stocks. The horizons of the project have expanded to include land-use within the whole catchment as it has become clear that many activities outside the riparian zone, such as drainage and clearfelling, impact upon the river. The work has only started and it will be a challenge to keep the momentum going.

Sources of help and advice? There are many skills within the Partnership- farming, forestry, river management and engineering. Perhaps the greatest skill is local knowledge, both of the river and of the way local people think, their perspectives and needs.

Some technical skills have been brought in, mainly through associated organisations such as SEPA and SNH. A forestry consultant was employed to survey a section of the river and advise on felling licences. The FE Civil Engineer provided advice on erosion sites together with possible costs. Various technical reports, such as that on the Urquhart Bay woods, have been consulted.

Helpful organisations have included SEPA, SNH, the Ness District Fisheries Board, Highland Council and the Forestry Commission.

The funds raised to date have been limited and further funding is being actively pursued. The principal contributors have been the riparian owners themselves (in addition to their own costs) and Highland Council. No training has taken place to date.

Future Activities? The short-term proposals have been largely completed and work is developing on the medium and long-term phases. The project can be summarised as on-going monitoring and constructive intervention in catchment management. There is no end point. The project is building up to a higher level of activity, defining key areas for action and obtaining funds to enable operations to take place. A target of 5-10 years has been set to sort out the major problems on the two rivers.

The Partnership group is able to co-opt new members should someone with the right skills make themselves available. If the group membership drops, the Community Council could call another public meeting and recruit some additional members. At present, the current group is functioning well and is pleased with progress. The members are pragmatic and realise that it will take time to improve the river to the optimum state.

Gordon Menzies

Glen Urquart Land Use Partnership

Temple Pier

Drumnadrochit IV63 6XR

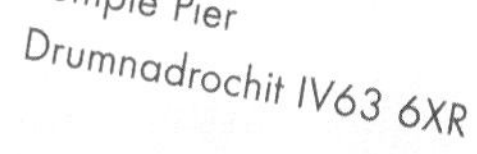

Lessons for others?

- Don't give up.
- Be prepared to compromise.
- Be prepared for a long haul.

Kelty and Blairadam

Summary

- Kelty and Blairadam Forest lie on either side of the M90 between the Forth Bridge and Perth
- Blairadam Forest extends to 2584 hectares, mainly commercial larch and pine approaching the end of the first rotation plus 30% broadleaves.
- The forest is owned and managed by Forest Enterprise with input from the local community, especially on the trails.
- The Heritage Trails group manages the project on behalf of the Kelty Partnership.
- The Kelty Partnership is a partnership of organisations, some community and others from local government, with an interest in the Kelty area.
- The key aim is to develop work opportunities whilst improving Kelty's image.
- The project was born in 1997.

Kelty and Blairadam

Why? The Kelty Heritage Trails project represents the coming together of a variety of different initiatives in the area. Perhaps the most potent of these was the Lindsay Memorial Committee, composed of ex-miners, who had raised funds to erect a memorial and a statue to those killed in a local mining disaster. They were looking for a suitable way of using the remaining funds to commemorate the local mining industry whilst improving the outlook of the local community.

At the same time several other things were happening. The Kelty Partnership, including Fife Council, was looking for projects to improve the social and economic conditions in the village. Fife Council Planning Services was looking at developing footpath and cycle routes in the area and Forest Enterprise was consulting with local people over the management of the adjoining Blairadam Forest. The Lochore Meadows Ranger Service had had their remit extended to cover land outside of the Country Park.

Who? Kelty is located beside the M90, midway between Edinburgh and Perth. It has a population of 5500 with very strong links to the mining industry. As with all former mining communities, there is high unemployment and related social and economic problems. Yet there is a strong sense of community and in recent years a plethora of community development groups have arisen.

Foremost amongst these is the Kelty Partnership which is a partnership between various organisations operating in Kelty. It sets up sub-groups to target specific initiatives. One such is the Special Projects Group which has the aims of improving the environment, raising awareness, improving access to the countryside, promoting interest in the rich local heritage and catering for the needs of people with disabilities. It has 16 members on its Board of Management and its own simple constitution. This group came up with the idea of developing a network of trails around the village to actively involve the community and attract visitors to the area. The Kelty Heritage Trails project was born in 1997.

The secretary of the Lindsay Memorial Committee, Archie Campbell, himself a retired miner, became the chair of the Heritage Trails project. He commented, 'people gave generously towards remembering the Lindsay disaster and we feel that it is appropriate to acknowledge the social, economic and environmental impact of mining in this area. Hopefully, our contribution will enable the Committee to secure other funding and we certainly intend to participate in this venture.'

What? Most of the proposed trails link westwards, across the M90, to the adjoining Forest Enterprise's Blairadam Forest and extend through part of that forest. Other proposed trails run eastwards to link with Lochore Meadows Country Park.

The forest, which extends to 2584 hectares, consists mainly of commercial conifer species managed as a crop, but there are some mixed areas, high in wildlife value, especially along the burnsides.

Larch accounts for 45% of the area, pines 20% and broadleaves (with beech predominating) for nearly 30%. Most of the conifers are approaching harvesting. There is also evidence of old mineworkings.

Vision? The long term vision for the project is ambitious; the development of the trails is just a start. Together with the trails are associated artworks, play areas and picnic sites. A Heritage Interpretation Centre is being planned as well as a permanent educational/ arts resource in the forest. Most excitingly, is the possible development of community controlled businesses linked to the trails. These businesses will complement existing businesses in the area. The details are in the Business Plan 1999 - 2002.

The group believes that the poor image of Kelty (home of the Kelty Clippie) is undeserved and can be greatly improved through the Heritage Trails and other projects. The natural resources of the area and its industrial heritage are excellent and can be managed to draw in visitors from the surrounding towns and Edinburgh. Already the nearby Butterchurn restaurant and craft centre attracts 120000 people per year, Lochore Meadows Country Park 325000 people per year. As the visitors increase, it is hoped this will encourage an improvement in the facilities of the town and a boost to local businesses.

Archie Campbell described how the forest is rich in memories and stories for the local people; how his father and grandfather took him for walks there when he was young and told him about the characters out of Sir Walter Scott's novels who are associated with the area.

The objectives for the project are laid out in the Business Plan:

1. Improve Kelty's image.
2. Develop work opportunities.
3. Encourage community participation.
4. Improve the local environment.
5. Record the social, industrial and natural heritage of Kelty.
6. Establishment of links with other areas.
7. Cater for special needs groups.

How? The project began when Kelty Partnership set up its Special Projects Group which then adopted the Heritage Trails concept as its first project. The woodland continues to belong to Forest Enterprise (FE) which is very open to approaches from the local community. Representatives of FE have been attending meetings of the Heritage Trails group since the idea was first mooted. The FE Land Agent plays a key role in drawing up the permissions.

The **milestones** have been:

1. Setting up the project in 1997.
2. The support of the Lindsay Memorial Committee.
3. The preparation of the Heritage Trails Business Plan 1999-2000.
4. A successful (despite the rain) Smashing Brashing Day in April 1999 with brashing footpaths, woodturning, Pictish art, stone drilling, medieval weaving and Victorian feather writing.
5. The signing of the partnership agreement with Fife Council's Vocational Training Section in December 1999.

Progress has been smooth to date, partly due to Fife's track record with community development projects. One **challenge** quoted was the delay of organisations in replying to funding applications. This can play havoc with the projected cashflow.

Greatest achievements? It's a bit early to say, but the group is pleased with the support of the community and of all the partner organisations. The majority of the management group turn up at every meeting and everyone including the local councillor seems to want to support this popular project. The challenging part is maintaining communications with such a wide group of interested parties.

Sources of help and advice? Many skills reside within the group and the Community Education Service which supports it. Specialised interests include rambling, local heritage and youth groups. One of the greatest skills is knowing who the key people are in different organisations and being able to ensure steady progress.

The group itself is supported by the partner organisations of the Kelty Partnership which includes all the relevant sections of Fife Council, such as the Economic Development Service. All of these organisations have been found to be helpful. There is also a good working relationship developing with Forest Enterprise, which has safeguarded footpaths during felling activities and consulted over restocking plans. Other landowners affected by the proposals have been consulted at an early stage.

External training in a wide range of skills has been provided to ten local people.

Funding has been obtained from a wide variety of sources- Fife Environment Trust, East of Scotland European Programme (Rechar), Fife Enterprise, the Employment Service (via New Deal), SNH and the miners' memorial fund. The Scottish Rights of Way Society has offered to put up sign posts, paid for by the Scottish Sports Council. Forest Enterprise will be carrying out a great deal of the associated work. Raising funds has been helped by the existence of the Partnership.

A key part of Phase 1 is the provision of ten New Deal places for local long term unemployed young people. They will be paid the going wage for the

job. As well as the 'development of work skills within a challenging work environment', the participants will be given every help to get permanent work. The project will act as a stepping stone to give the participants an employment history, customised training (partially at college), job search training and placements.

Future activities? The project is in three phases with the first phase due to start in January 2000. Phase 1 projects include:

- The development of the initial trails in Blairadam Forest with the construction and upgrading of paths, provision of signs and panels, construction of bridges and planting of shrubs.
- The development of work opportunities for long term unemployed Kelty residents under New Deal funding.
- Promotion of local businesses and the establishment of a traders' association.
- The painting of a mural on a motorway bridge, the installation of sculptures, the design of the interpretation panels and a community video.
- The publication of an information leaflet and placing of promotional material elsewhere.

Phase 2 takes the project further with:

- Further trails into the forest and linking with Lochore Meadows.
- Development of a Heritage Interpretation Centre.
- Development of community controlled businesses.
- Development of barbecue areas, play areas and a youth shelter.
- Employment of a part-time ranger
- Further arts installations and residencies.

Phase 3 is as far forward as the business plan looks with:

- Starting up the community businesses.
- Development of a permanent educational/ arts resource.
- Development of links to wider features and visitor attractions.
- Further arts developments.

This is a major project which is expected to make a significant difference to the quality of life, employment prospects and economic viability of the local community. As such, it is expected to run on until its various parts become self-sustaining. Enthusiasm in the local community is high at present and this is underpinned by the active participation of the partner organisations. Individuals in the management group are likely to come and go and the constitution helps to ensure continuity.

Contacts

Kate Stewart
Kelty Partnership
(Special Projects Group)

Kelty Community Centre
Main Street, Kelty, Fife KY4 0AQ

Lessons for others? The lesson is to work with as many interested parties as possible and to somehow give them all a sense of ownership of the project. The fact that the project is embedded in the local community is vital.

Knoydart

Summary

- The Knoydart Forest Trust project area covers the west of the Knoydart peninsula.
- The woodland area extends to 500 ha mixed conifer plantation and 100 ha native broadleaved woodland in 10 different ownerships, the largest of whom is the Knoydart Foundation.
- The Knoydart Forest Trust runs the project.
- The Trust manages the Knoydart Foundation's woodlands through a management agreement.
- The Trust is a company limited by guarantee with charitable status.
- The key aim is to help strengthen the local economy.
- Work started in the woodlands in the summer of 1999.

Knoydart

Why? The community of Knoydart is one of the most remote in Scotland. Access is by boat or 'the long walk in'. In many ways it is more remote than many of the islands despite being a peninsula. There is a troubled history of land use and qualities of self-reliance are required to live there. The project was started in order to enable the local people to manage one of the natural resources, the Knoydart woodlands, in a way that would deliver benefits in terms of stable local employment, returns to the local economy and improvements in wildlife diversity. This aspiration was obvious in the wake of a succession of landowners with short term interests, resulting in a rapid turnover of people and trees. The future now looks more secure and prosperous.

Who? The project is for the resident community who will benefit through employment and a strengthened local economy and for the wider public who will enjoy a better managed natural environment and improved access.

The community might be described as everyone with a commitment to the place and its people. The Trust was established as a company limited by guarantee with charitable status. The core members of the Trust are resident members. Membership is open and the resident members elect the directors/trustees annually on a rotational basis.

The directors/trustees manage the Trust directly and employ Grant Holroyd as the Community Forester. His time is split between administration/management/supervision and forestry work.

What? The project area extends to about 11 000 ha of mostly open hill with 3 main conifer plantations and scattered remnants of native woodland:-

1. 250 ha 20 year old "failed commercial" lodgepole pine /Sitka spruce on the hill.
2. 250 ha mixed conifer & native broadleaves around the main village of Inverie. This includes some quality timber and ancient semi-natural woodland as well as prolific Rhododendron ponticum. The conifer plantation is 25-60+ years old and has been under-managed for the past 25 years.
3. 100 ha outlying native woodland remnants, which are generally not regenerating due to grazing pressure.

The woodlands cover ten landholdings. The main one is now owned by the Knoydart Foundation (a partnership of Knoydart Community Association, Highland Council, John Muir Trust, Chris Brasher Trust, Kilchoan Estate and HIE).

The objectives for the woodlands are to:

- secure, expand and maintain the genetic integrity of the existing native woodland remnants
- re-structure the failed commercial plantations to increase their landscape and habitat value
- bring into management the mixed woodlands around Inverie village to provide locally useful quality timber, habitat diversity and public access.

Vision? The vision of the project is 'to deliver quality woodland management through an integrated long term management plan that will realise the potential of our environment and community.'

The management plan brings together the different landholdings and attempts to redress the neglect and loss of woodlands in the past by harnessing local commitment and enthusiasm.

The specific objectives are to:

- produce a long term plan (achieved)
- secure a management agreement with Knoydart Foundation (achieved)
- secure management agreements with other relevant landholders
- provide training as required (ongoing)
- secure funding (ongoing)
- implement the various components of the plan (started).

How? Funding allowed a consultant to be employed to help with the first management and business plans (at that time the community didn't actually know who owned Knoydart Estate which included the main woodland area). After much debacle and a few surprises, in March 1999 the Knoydart Foundation managed to buy Knoydart Estate from the receivers with money from a public appeal, John Muir Trust (JMT), Chris Brasher Trust, HIE, Scottish Natural Heritage (SNH), Cameron Mackintosh and an anonymous donor. By this time the Forest Trust had been established and the woodland plan was ready to be implemented. The Forest Trust now manages the Foundation's woodland through a management agreement based on the management plan. The other landholders within the project area have been encouraging and discussions regarding future woodland management are ongoing.

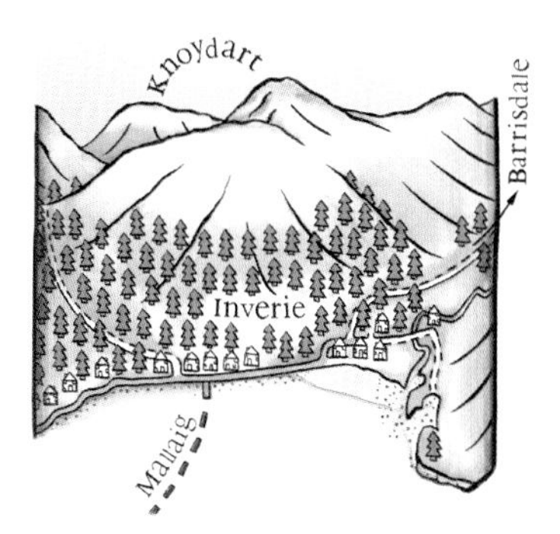

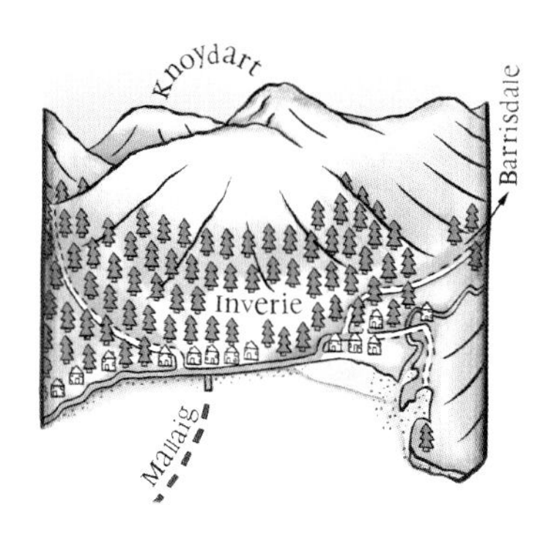

The **milestones** have been:

1. Funding for management and business plans was secured in January 1998.
2. An acceptable management plan was produced in August 1998.
3. The Rural Challenge Fund application was applied for in October 1998.
4. The application was assessed in January 1999.
5. The application was notified as unsuccessful in April 1999.
6. Objective One funding with co-funding from SNH, Lochaber Limited, Highland Council and JMT secured the public access component of the plan in June 1999.
7. Woodland Grant Scheme was applied for in October 1999.
8. A management agreement with the Knoydart Foundation was completed in Dec 1999.
9. The public access component of the plan- clearing rhododendrons, removing redundant fencing and pathwork was started in November 1999.

The **challenges** have taken the form of a constant barrage of hoops, usually provided by government agencies, which require not only jumping through, but somersaults and backflips in the form of business plans, forest design plans, woodland management plans, training plans, consultation, scoping, interviews, networking, coffee and biscuits....etc.

The **solution** is to keep jumping, ignore the ones that are out of reach and never turn down a cup of coffee. The biggest headache is running several funders side by side, all of whom have different needs, procedures and methods of claiming biscuits.

Sources of help and advice? Within the local group there are two ex-estate foresters, a retired submariner, a sheep farmer, a social worker and several enthusiastic volunteers. The Trust has had the help of Andrew Campbell (JMT Woodland Manager) and a very patient business adviser who has given his time voluntarily. The Trust employed a forestry consultant Iain MacLennan to help with the initial management and business plans. He still helps out when asked and deserves a special mention for his patience and help. An accountant and a lawyer are also employed as required.

Individuals within the Forestry Commission and other agencies have been of great help. Whilst ultimately their support has been invaluable, the bureaucracy and slow pace of response of the Scottish Office /Executive Highlands and Islands Partnership Programme and the Forestry Commission have been both frustrating and debilitating.

The main funders so far are EAGGF (Objective One), JMT, SNH, HIE, Lochaber Limited and Highland Council. Often several funders have had to be applied to for the same piece of work which represents a huge administrative effort for a small largely voluntary organisation. The Trust has suggested that a scoping meeting of the main funders could be used to allocate funds for a project and lead to a single application. Other funds and resources have come from private individuals, volunteers and timber sales. It is hoped that funds generated by the project will gradually replace funds from outside.

There is a training plan and the Community Forester has been studying at the Scottish School of Forestry since September 1999.

Future Activities? Activities fall into several areas. On the practical front, there will be seed collection and the establishment of a small tree nursery, fencing, planting and regeneration of native woodland, management of the existing woodlands, restructuring of the plantations and the development of value added products using the felled timber. To support this will be training in chainsaws, machine operation and first aid. A necessary evil is the paperwork-funding applications, grant claim forms and cashflow projections.

The project will continue as long as people make use of the woodlands. The optimal level of activity depends on what the woodlands and the community can sustain. This remains to be determined.

Lessons for Others? Many lessons have already been learned. These include:

- Be open and transparent with your community. Make a point of identifying the thorny issues early on.
- If you use consultants make sure they understand what you are asking them to do. Agree a brief before you take them on and hold them to it. Don't be afraid to get comparative quotes (you don't have to choose the cheapest). If you expect work to be done by a certain individual, make sure this is clear and stated in the brief.
- Don't allow consultants, agencies or professionals to take over. Remember they work for you. Don't let them discuss your business amongst themselves without referring back to you.
- Avoid 100% funding from one source.
- Use your own time as co-funding - this helps you to retain ownership of the project as well as showing a true account of costs.
- The more unrestricted/private cash you can find the better (£1 cash is worth a lot more that £1 of grant).
- Beware of complications - don't be afraid to turn down potential funding offers if you don't like the terms, or if their claim procedures are too cumbersome. Remember funders get paid to give you money. It should be noted that the Objective One application process is easier than the subsequent technicalities and claim procedure.
- Lack of capital to get started and funding for management costs at the outset can be a real problem.
- It always takes longer than you think - but keep at it and maintain focus and determination.

Grant Holroyd
Community Forester

Knoydart Forest Trust
Inverie
Knoydart PH41 4PL

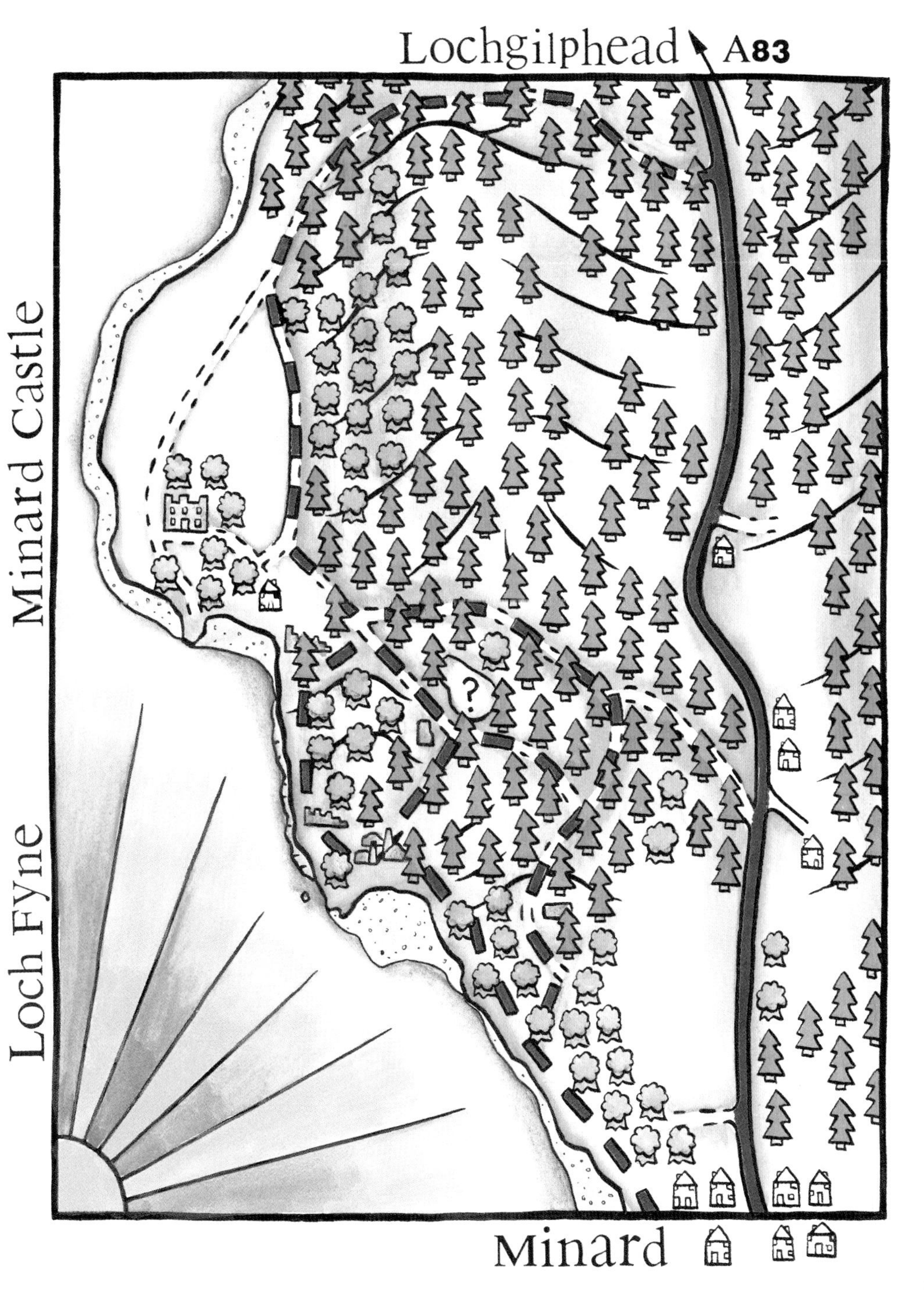

Summary

- Minard Community Woodland is located on the west shore of Loch Fyne in Argyll.
- It extends to 170 hectares, dominated by semi-mature conifers, but with 25% broadleaves and open ground.
- Minard Community Woodland Trust manages the project in partnership with Forest Enterprise.
- The Trust is a company limited by guarantee with charitable status.
- The key aims are recreation, education, social and economic benefits.
- The project began in 1997.

Minard

Why? At a meeting of the West Loch Fyne Community Council in August 1997, the matter of the imminent proposed disposal of Minard Castle woodlands by Forest Enterprise (FE) was discussed for the first time. The community had been comfortable with public ownership and was suspicious that private ownership could throw up difficulties such as loss of access. The Community Council began to consider the advantages of community control.

A small steering group was set up to explore possibilities. Amongst its members was Bill Middlemiss, the current Company Secretary for the Minard Community Woodland Trust (MCWT). He, and the Argyll and Bute Countryside Trust, had been aware since 1992 of the possibility that the woodlands might be disposed of by FE and had looked into access agreements.

Who? The project is mainly for the people of Minard and the surrounding area. About 240 people live in Minard, quite a number of these in the 17 houses located adjacent to the Minard Castle woodlands. The population has now got a good age structure with young and older families as well as older people. Many of the working adults work in Lochgilphead which is the regional administrative centre with local government offices, a secondary school and a hospital. The local economy is described as 'leaky' with 95% of the income coming in from outside and 95% being spent outside the village. There is a village shop taken on recently by a young family, a primary school and a voluntary fire station. It is hoped that the community woodlands will help to support the local economy and keep these facilities open.

The West Loch Fyne Community Council covers both Minard and Lochgair to the south. It is fairly active and representative of the two communities. Its Woodland Sub-committee, referred to above, became formalised as the Minard Community Woodland Trust once it was time to begin the fundraising process. This is a company limited by guarantee with charitable status. There are 56 members of the Trust, each of whom pays £1 for membership. The members elect the Trustees at the AGM. The Trustees are the driving force for the project.

What? Minard Castle woodlands extend to 170 hectares and are located between the public road (A83) and the sea to the south of Minard village. The site was formerly estate policies planted largely with commercial conifers. The species breakdown is 50% Sitka spruce, 22% Norway spruce, 3% other conifers, 18% broadleaves (mainly birch, oak, beech and sycamore) and 7% other land. 28% of the trees were planted in the '80s, 72% in the '60s or earlier. The conifers are very productive with yield classes up to 22 cubic metres per hectare per year, mean annual increment.

There are other habitats within the woodland, mainly grassland and steep, rocky slopes. Several burns run through the wood and one low lying area lends itself to pond construction. The majority of the woodland is workable although the level of management in recent years has been very low. The District Valuer's (DV) valuation has been set at £315,000.

The objectives for the woodland have been established as:

1. Increase of the native woodland area to around 40%.
2. Retention and management of 75 ha of commercial forest.
3. Development of short rotation crops.
4. Removal of much of the rhododendron.
5. Creation and management of non-woodland habitats, such as a pond.
6. Development of associated businesses.

Vision? The long term vision is for a sensitively managed hybrid forest, part commercial forest and part native woodland. The commercial forest would continue to be based on high yielding Sitka and Norway spruce and Western hemlock. The native woodland areas, which are located towards the Minard end and along the shore, lend themselves more readily to improved access trails, including the proposed Heritage Trail, and other forms of recreation. They would link into a potential Forest Habitat Network, rich in native woodlands, running along the Loch Fyne shoreline. A significant number of local jobs would be created through woodland operations, support activities and associated commercial developments. These jobs would help to safeguard the local economy.

The aims of the project are "to bring recreational, educational, social and economic benefits to the local community. The woodland will provide a sustainable source of income, which can be used to manage the woodland and gradually bring these benefits to the community. The rich natural heritage and archaeological remains within this peaceful site provide opportunities to create and improve facilities for education and recreation, while maximising the potential of the land through re-zoning it for various uses, which will provide opportunities for commercial operations to create new jobs in this remote area."

As many as ten jobs could be generated through providing sites and services, making opportunities available for local businesses. Such businesses could include a tree nursery, a sawmill, a timber processing unit and holiday accommodation. It is hoped that an estate worker/ ranger might be directly employed and that any contractors would come from as close to the village as possible.

How? The project started with the perceived threat of a FE disposal which soon came to be seen as a tremendous opportunity. Since the formation of the Woodland Sub-committee in August '97, the following milestones have been passed:

1. Discussions with interested groups such as the Argyll Green Woodworkers, Woodland Trust, Mid Argyll Natural History and Antiquarian Society, Rural Forum and SNH culminating in a site meeting in March '98.

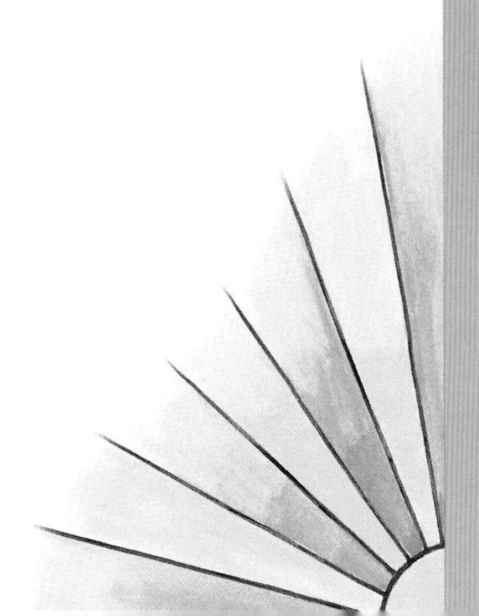

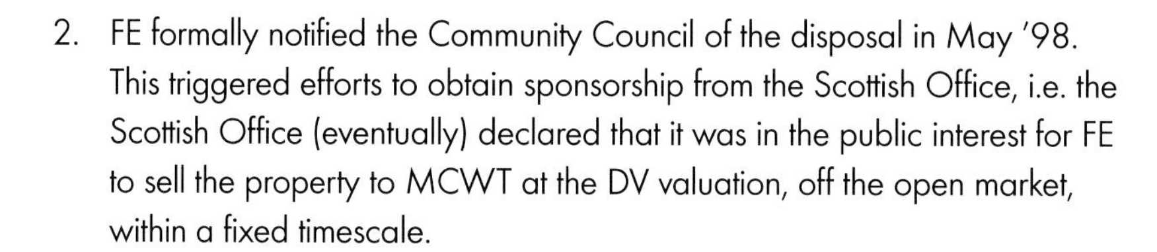

2. FE formally notified the Community Council of the disposal in May '98. This triggered efforts to obtain sponsorship from the Scottish Office, i.e. the Scottish Office (eventually) declared that it was in the public interest for FE to sell the property to MCWT at the DV valuation, off the open market, within a fixed timescale.
3. An initial valuation of the woodlands was carried out by Scottish Woodlands in June 1998.
4. A feasibility study by Scottish Woodlands and Bill Middlemiss was completed in December '98.
5. A meeting of the Woodlands Group in July '98 was attended by Lorna Campbell of the HIE Community Land Unit, who offered support to the project.
6. A well attended Open Meeting was held in the Village Hall in August '98. There was a display at which options were outlined, discussions, a questionnaire and a petition. There was 100% support for acquiring the woodlands and 72 signatures for the petition supporting the setting up of the Trust.
7. The DV valuation was announced in December '98.
8. The Minard Community Woodland Trust came into being in January '99.
9. A preliminary meeting was held with the Heritage Lottery Fund (HLF) in February '99.
10. Lord Sewell supported the application for Sponsorship in March '99.
11. The Scottish Office stated that it 'was minded to' grant sponsorship in April '99.
12. Application to HLF supported by a Business Plan was submitted in May '99.
13. Application was rejected in September '99.
14. Trustees met in October '99 to discuss whether the project is still viable.
15. Forest Enterprise offered a partnership agreement based on its new guidelines on working with communities and removed the woodlands from the disposals list.
16. A minute of the agreement has been signed for FE to manage the woodland jointly with MCWT.
17. A woodland management plan has been agreed.
18. The first timber coup has been harvested under the new agreement.

The biggest **challenges** have been:

- The rejection by HLF which may prove to be terminal to the project.
- In addition, the Scottish Office caused a great deal of difficulty by being unable to react positively or quickly on the issue of Sponsorship. It may have been caught by surprise and future applications by other groups may proceed more smoothly.
- The time required to develop the project has been almost all unpaid.
- The lack of an office open to local people.

Greatest achievements? "Getting as far as this." Building a team together, getting local support and working through the complexities of Sponsorship and fundraising with changing timescales have been the greatest challenges and the greatest achievements.

Sources of help and advice? The community has been fortunate with the range of skills present amongst the Trustees. These are listed as:

project management,
natural resource management,
administration,
interpretation,
community business,
estate management,
VAT administration,
public sector liaison,
public relations,
volunteer management,
fundraising,
access management,
training management,
farming,
footpath construction,
company secretary.

The skills which had to be brought in from outside were legal, accounting and commercial woodland management & valuation.

Forest Enterprise has been supportive of the project and shown flexibility in adjusting to the changing timescales forced upon the project by Scottish Office and HLF. The Community Land Unit has been supportive and come up with some funding for project development costs and a second valuation.

Fundraising has been the sticking point for the project. The bid to the HLF for £255,000 (75% of the initial project costs, including purchase) has been unsuccessful. The applications to other potential funders (HIE, SNH, various charitable trusts will depend upon whether the project can be repackaged. Early success with fundraising included £1000 from the Rural Initiatives Fund for the first Feasibility Study and support from the Community Land Unit. The Millennium Forest for Scotland Trust was deliberately avoided as it was believed that it wouldn't be flexible enough to deal with the changing timescales or the fact that the principal species are non-native.

The only training to date has been in footpath construction. One of the Trustees is currently enjoying (!) a six month training programme near Achnashellach.

Future activities? Assuming that the project goes forward in some form, the initial activity will be to publicise the project locally. A leaflet will be produced. The Heritage Trail is a priority providing improved access from the village to the woodland via archaeological sites such as the fascinating Solar Alignment and areas high in biodiversity. Habitat and species surveys will be carried out to gather baseline data. The bird interest is already well recorded.

Within the first six months, woodland management planning will commence with the sale of timber providing funds both for restocking and the implementation of community projects within the woodland and in the village (such as supporting the Village Hall).

There are other innovative plans to interpret the woodland and these will be developed once the project is secured.

There is no **end point** to the project. Once started, it is expected to last as long as the village itself. The **optimal level** of involvement will vary over the years depending upon the individual people within the community. The woodland will be there and local people will decide how heavily they wish to be involved. **Continuity** of active group members will occur through involvement. New people will surface and get involved gradually. It is the responsibility of the Trustees to provide different kinds of opportunities so that all ages and groups can enjoy a range of activities in the woodland. The Trust structure ensures that new Trustees are sought on an annual basis.

Lessons for others? There are several lessons which the group would like to share with others:

- Different people have different visions which need to be blended together. This is easier if the group vision isn't too clearly defined.
- The group has to accept all the responsibilities which go with the project.
- There must be cover for the key people developing the project.
- It all can take a lot of time.

Contacts

Bill Middlemiss
Company Secretary

Minard Community
Woodland Trust
Beannaichte, Lower Achagoyle,
Minard, Argyll PA32 8YD

Email: w.middlemiss@talk21.com

Newcastleton

Summary

- Newcastleton is located close to the English border between Hawick and Carlisle.
- It is close to several very large commercial spruce forests, including Kielder.
- These forests are managed primarily for softwood production but have additional objectives and a social remit.
- Copshaw Ltd, a 'community company', is developing the project.
- Copshaw Ltd is a company limited by guarantee with charitable status. It intends to set up a subsidiary trading company once the Combined Heat and Power plant gets the green light.
- The key aim is to use timber residues from the surrounding forests as a renewable resource to generate heat and power for the local community, thereby generating jobs, reducing pollution and improving health.
- The inspiration for the project came in spring 1995 and a full feasibility study is currently being prepared.

Newcastleton

Why? Newcastleton (formerly known as Copshaw) is a small isolated village near the border with England which has a tenuous power supply. Every winter there are long periods of powercuts. Yet the village is surrounded by a vast resource of fuel in the form of conifer plantations. The idea of developing this valuable resource had its birth at a post Rio Agenda 21 meeting in Edinburgh which led on to the setting up of the Borders Forum for Sustainability. The Newcastleton Community Council (NCC) sent a representative who was inspired by the Scandinavian experience in small local Combined Heat and Power (CHP) stations.

The advantages of cheap, dependable power using a local resource coupled with the health benefits from reducing coal smog and at the same time creating and supporting local jobs, sounded very attractive and the project was under way.

Who? The community was already well defined. The village is a mile long by a mile wide and home to 850 people. A further 450 people live around the village in Liddesdale. 60% of the population is over 60 and unemployment is high since the demise of the railway and the Barbour factory. Agriculture and forestry provide fewer jobs than before. There are a few forestry contractors living in the village (one team is currently working in Ireland) and four professional foresters. Now most of the employment is in services and in the towns of Hawick and Carlisle.

Fortunately, the sense of community in the village is strong. For example there is always an election for the Community Council with a regular turnout of over 30%. The community regularly raises many thousands of pounds for local and national charities. The bicentenary of the village was in 1993 and the celebrations, organised by the NCC, were very well supported.

The NCC has an enlightened attitude to projects; it sets them up and then encourages them to become independent. An energy sub-committee was formed, then after the first public meeting it became a steering group with a mandate from that meeting. Three members of the steering group are now the Directors of Copshaw Limited, a company limited by guarantee with charitable status. Copshaw Ltd will in turn set up a subsidiary trading company to trade in heat and power. Its profits will be covenanted to Copshaw Ltd to create a Common Good Fund which will support a variety of exciting community projects. As well as the Directors, several other local people with particular skills and knowledge sit on the management team. These include the local electrician and plumber and the secretary of the Old People's Welfare Committee. There is now a Project Manager, Gill Buchanan, who works out of an office in the centre of the village.

What? To the north, east and south of Newcastleton lie very large commercial plantations, mostly owned by Forest Enterprise (FE) and dominated by Sitka spruce. These include Wauchope, Newcastleton, Kershope and Kielder Forests which together form the largest area of planted forest in northern Europe. The largest, Kielder Forest across the border in England, is now in its full production phase. The nearest, Newcastleton Forest, has been heavily harvested over the last 20 years and is still productive as the young trees grow towards economic maturity again. One issue is that on very poor wet sites, the brash is left on the ground to provide access for vehicles and to put nutrients back into the system. However, other forest products such as small roundwood and tops could be available, at the market price with low haulage costs, as fuel for a CHP scheme.

The primary objective for these large plantations is softwood timber production with other objectives, environmental and social, recognised. Recent FE policy in Scotland has taken on board 'making a greater commitment to rural development and local jobs'. Rural development is also a main theme of the England Forestry Strategy.

Copshaw Ltd hasn't yet approached the forest managers with a view to securing sources of supply and hasn't, unlike other RDF projects, any control over the resource. Yet should the CHP project be successful the destinies of the community and the forest will be much more closely tied than before. The forest will be the natural resource upon which the well-being of the local community is founded.

Vision? The long-term vision of the project is to get the CHP plant up and running, then to develop 'add-on' businesses as appropriate, limited only by imagination and resources. There are several perceived benefits:-

- A more reliable electricity supply
- Affordable heating for local people (one aim is to heat the homes of elderly people for the same cost as they heat one room at present)
- Reduction in local pollution by reducing coal burning (some days the pollution levels are higher than the worst parts of Edinburgh and Glasgow)
- Reduction in global pollution by substituting renewable wood for coal
- The development of a new tourist attraction
- Additional employment opportunities
  - Directly associated with the plant- operational, maintenance, fuel supply, meter reading, billing, etc.
  - Indirectly through new businesses attracted to the area through cheaper heat and power, such as horticulture and brewing.
  - Indirectly through the development of green tourism based on a visitor centre
- Additional community benefits through a Common Good Fund supporting local initiatives such as
  - A health centre
  - Buying up holiday homes as they become available to make them available again for young families

How? It is taking time for such an innovative project to get under way and there have been a few setbacks along the way. The inspirational seminar on alternative technology was in spring 1995. Since then the **milestones** have been:

1. The NCC decided that the CHP idea was worth pursuing and invited speakers to an open meeting.
2. The open meeting was held during summer 1995 with speakers from the Energy Technical Support Unit (ETSU) and Borders Biofuels (BB).
3. Scottish Borders Enterprise (SBE) agreed to fund a preliminary survey to ascertain the level of interest. In August 1995, 400 questionnaires were circulated round the village. Half were returned and of these 93% were in favour with none against the idea.
4. A public meeting was held soon after. It was attended by 100 local people plus representatives from the Borders Planning Department & Environmental Health, Forest Enterprise, SBE and Buccleuch Estates. The meeting agreed that the project was worth pursuing and appointed the steering group.
5. ETSU, SBE and Scottish Enterprise (SE) agreed to fund a feasibility study. SBE dealt with the contractual arrangements and Borders Biofuels were commissioned in spring 1996 to carry out the study. Their remit was to consult with the community; to answer the basic questions posed by the steering group and to present their findings to the community at an exhibition.
6. Unfortunately, the consultants weren't experienced in working with communities and there was poor communication between them and the steering group. The exhibition was not 'community friendly' and had to be salvaged at the last minute by the intervention of the steering group.
7. In the end, the exhibition held in November 1996 in the village hall was a success, demonstrating that a CHP plant could work and achieve all the benefits with few problems. Over 300 people attended the exhibition. 150 households were prepared to sign up to the project.
8. The final report due at the same time as the exhibition wasn't in fact made available until July 1997. Worse still, it was poorly presented, difficult to understand, didn't address some of the key issues and came to different conclusions than those presented at the exhibition i.e. the heat should come from wood and the electricity from diesel oil.
9. The NCC decided to press on with a wood-only combined scheme, but valuable momentum had been lost.
10. In April 1998 the community company Copshaw Limited was set up and achieved charitable status.
11. In October 1998, SBE/SE found some more money and the Project Manager post was advertised.
12. The Project Manager was appointed in February 1999.

13. The tender document for feasibility study Mark II (to answer the questions not answered in Mark I) was prepared and put out to tender in August 1999. To ensure that this time all the implications of a biomass fuelled CHP plant would be examined in depth, four disciplines were involved- engineering, architecture, quantity surveying and planning.
14. The key engineering contract was awarded to Scottish Power Technology based in East Kilbride who are currently looking at the technical options in advance of the full feasibility study.
15. The results of the Technical Options Review were presented in Feb/ March 2000.

There have been several major **challenges** which include:

- Funding and especially synchronised matching funding. Many people in organisations have become quite excited about the project, but have then admitted that their organisations aren't able to support it financially. The project has been turned down for Lottery funding and by Lloyds/ TSB, although the former has been helpful and has invited the group to reapply. Other possible sources of funding such as the CHP Agency have yet to decide on whether they can offer financial support.
- Taking on the wrong consultants for the first Feasibility Study, largely due to not being expert in the subject. This mistake was compounded by the consultants relating to SBE, who dealt with the contract, rather than the community steering group whose project it was. This resulted in a poor report and a serious loss of momentum from which the group is just recovering.
- Related to this is the lack of expertise in CHP from which the group suffered in the early stages. Latterly, the situation has greatly improved with the involvement of the Centre for the Economic Review of Power Development (CERPD) based at Glasgow and Strathclyde Universities which has been providing friendly and impartial advice.

Greatest Achievements? To be still going after 5 years despite the setbacks is a great achievement. The Directors believe that they now have skilled consultants developing the project and that local people are still patiently supportive. The great potential benefits of the project make all the effort worthwhile.

Fundraising has been challenging. It involves working with a range of organisations, each with its own characteristics. All the time, at least one eye has to be kept on the local community, making sure it is kept informed of developments and is firmly behind the project team.

Sources of Help and Advice? The skills represented within the management team include having the vision for the project, community links, contacts, local technical knowledge of power and plumbing, public relations, legal and organisational skills.

The skills which needed to be brought in were mainly technical as well as project management.

Many organisations have been helpful including SBE, Scottish Borders Council, CERPD, the Energy Saving Trust, Scottish Homes and Scottish Power Technology. Funding has come from SBE, SE and Leader II with a number of applications to other organisations currently being considered.

Apart from some specialised training, for instance in processing tenders, the management team has brought a wealth of knowledge and experience to the project.

Future Activities? After the results of the full feasibility study have been presented to, and understood by, the local community, a democratic decision will be taken as to whether the benefits are sufficient to justify embarking on this pioneering enterprise.

The project will then need to develop contracts or partnerships with Forest Enterprise (on both sides of the Border) and/or other forest owners for the supply of suitable material for fuelling the plant, and Scottish Power for the use of the power lines. Already FE has welcomed the development of a potential new market on its doorstep and is open to approaches from the community. The forest represents a vast renewable resource for the community. Harnessing the energy will contribute greatly to the development of the local economy.

The CHP project will be completed when the Directors 'switch on heat and power to the village from its own local power station.'

Phase II will be on-going, bringing new vitality into the community through business opportunities and green tourism. Copshaw Ltd is confident that more people will become involved as the project becomes increasingly real and relevant to local people.

Contacts

David Mackey
Chairman

Copshaw Ltd
27 Langholm Street
Newcastleton TD9 0QX

E-mail: david.mackey@care4free.net

Lessons for Others?

- The community must be clear about its objectives from the very beginning.
- Independent technical advice should be secured as soon as possible. Funds for this should be acquired on the basis that the advisor is working solely for the community.
- It is essential to ensure that local people are on board throughout.
- Don't give up !

Footnote

The project has come to an end through lack of funding. A sum of £20,000 was raised towards turning the results of the options study into a costed, developable scheme, but the balance of £40,000 remained unfunded.

Newton Mearns

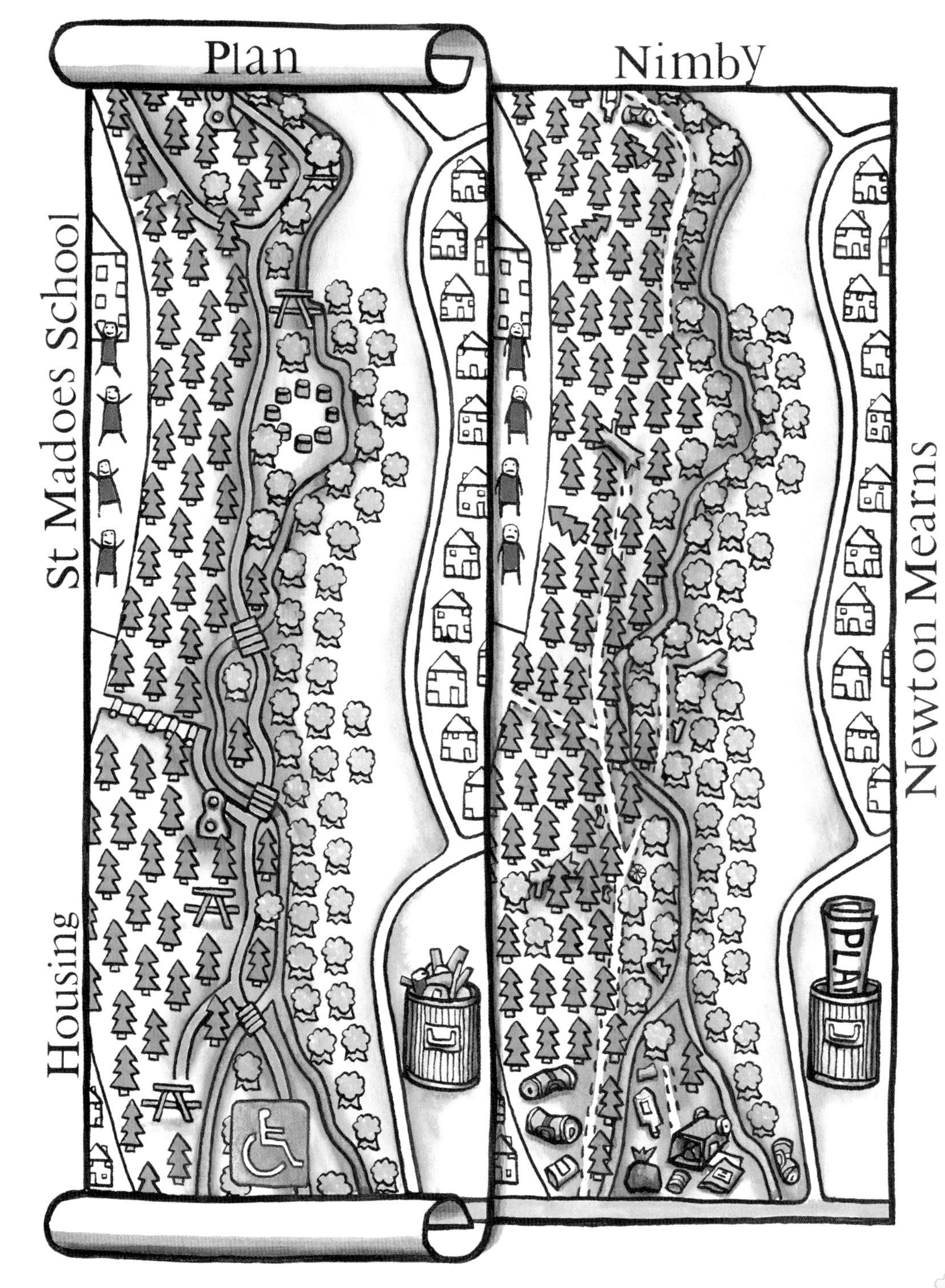

Summary

- The project is located close to Newton Mearns, south of Glasgow.
- The woodland covers 5 hectares, two thirds of which are 25 year old conifers and one third older broadleaves. A stream runs through the wood and there are a number of open glades.
- The woodland was to be managed by the community whilst continuing to be owned by the local council.
- The project was developed by a sub-committee of the community council.
- The community council is a recognised body, part of local government.
- The key aims were to maintain and develop a beautiful habitat for the benefit of local people whilst providing work opportunities.
- The project began early in 1998 and ended in September 1999.

Newton Mearns

Why? The idea of developing the Capelrig Nature Path came up in early 1998. The Community Council had accrued some finances and was looking for ways to mark the Millennium. A competition was held to gather ideas for a Millennium Project.

The winning idea was to develop Capelrig wood as a community asset by building a path through the woodland, suitable for disabled access. The project included bringing the woodland under a management plan, developing both timber and non-timber woodland resources and providing educational and nature interpretation facilities.

The involvement of the wider community resulted from various informal contacts by members of the Community Council.

Who? Capelrig Nature Path was intended to benefit people throughout the community and to provide training opportunities for young people to help them into work. There are few other natural or recreational facilities in the area. The community served by the Community Council is approximately 25,000 strong in the suburban residential areas of Newton Mearns and Whitecraigs, south of Glasgow.

The Community Council is made up of 24 members with co-opted members from the local Legion and Horticultural Society. Anyone interested in becoming a member can be voted onto the Community Council. Meetings are attended by 3-4 local Councillors and are open to the public. Information is disseminated by informal mechanisms and by posting information in public places such as libraries and the local press. A sub-committee of 5 members was set up to oversee the Millennium Project.

What? The woodland is approximately 5 hectares in size and lies within a residential area. It forms a corridor, 100 metres wide by 500 metres in length, along the Capelrig Burn. The boundaries of the wood are formed by roads on three sides. On the fourth side a school forms two thirds of the boundary and the remainder is housing.

The area is owned by East Renfrewshire Council. It is mostly woodland with a species rich ground flora. One third is mixed broadleaves with sycamore, ash, elm, goat willow and hawthorn. Two thirds of the wood is Scots pine and spruce plantation. There are also open glades and grass areas along the south edge. A lack of management has resulted in a delightful natural diversity of flora and fauna which is of high nature conservation and amenity value. The value of the site has been endorsed by several organisations which have been involved in developing the Capelrig Nature Path project including the East Renfrewshire Council, Scottish Wildlife Trust (SWT), SNH and the Forestry Commission.

The recent history of the woodland is not well known. It is thought that the plantation was established just before the surrounding housing developments, about 25 years ago. The broadleaved woodland is a lot older. The site has a long history. The remains of a Celtic cross have been excavated just to the NE of the woodland. This dates from the 1st Millennium and is now in the care of the Kelvingrove Museum.

There had been no management of the woodland and no thinning of the plantation. Following the storms in January 1999 the Community Council undertook some clearance of damaged trees with support from East Renfrewshire Council.

Vision? The vision of the project was to utilise a beautiful natural asset and to encourage the local community to be more aware of it and involved with it. It was hoped that involvement in the wood would bring the different generations together.

The initial objectives were:

Recreation & amenity - To build a path through the wood, including three bridges over the Capelrig Burn, all suitable for disabled access. This would eventually be linked to other path networks being developed through the region, by SUSTRANS and East Renfrewshire Council, linking with other national networks. The building of the path would be undertaken by local young people on the New Deal scheme. Secondly, to landscape the area and develop a garden to be enjoyed by people with disabilities, wood sculptures, picnic areas, children's activity area and dog walking area.

Woodland management - To manage the woodland by thinning and brashing as necessary, removing obstructive and dangerous timber. Resources such as timber, firewood and chips would be utilised wherever appropriate.

Education - To encourage greater awareness of the nature conservation interest and history associated with the wood. There were plans to build an open air classroom from stumps of felled trees and to place information boards at suitable points

How? Information about the competition was informally spread through the community and advertised in the local free press, the normal method of disseminating Community Council information. The project had the full support of the woodland owner, East Renfrewshire Council. A sub-committee was formed to steer the project forward. Several community organisations became involved, such as local schools (supported by the Director of Education), Scouts, parents and many local residents.

The progress of the project took three different lines- fundraising/ planning, design and events.

Fund raising and planning - This was undertaken by the sub-committee and progressed over several months. Fundraising and planning happened hand-in-hand as various organisations offered advice and further contacts. Planning included discussion and costing on the design of the landscaping, path and bridge creation and woodland management. The development of the fundraising was initially piecemeal. Various funding opportunities were investigated, but the commitments required by some funders and the need for matching funding caused a certain amount of anxiety for the sub-committee. Eventually, a substantial offer came, via SWT, from a local waste management company, Biffa, which offered a 'landfill tax' award.

School design competition - the local children developed their own ideas for the landscaping of the woodland and path. This encouraged the children to consider the opportunities that the project could offer the community as well as learning more about the wood.

Litter pick-up/barbecue events - two very successful and enjoyable litter pick-up days were held. These helped to bring the community together and increased awareness of the potential of the project.

In the summer of 1998 an attempt was made to set up a 'Friends of Newton Mearns' environmental group with the aim of influencing issues of concern about the area, including the Capelrig Nature Path. Unfortunately the group didn't form due to lack of interest. The **milestones** have been:

- April 1998 - Competition for Millennium Project.
- May 1998 - Decision to take forward Capelrig Nature Park.
- June 1998 - Site visit by the sub-committee.
- June 1998 - Fundraising and planning began.
- Oct 1998 - Yellow pages 'Make a difference Day' litter pick-up was attended by 30 people.
- Oct 1998 - Schools undertook designs for the paths.
- March 1999 - SWT offered to apply for a Biffaward which could offer significant funding.
- May 1999 - Litter Pick-up and barbecue attended by 84 people. This was very successful, but was the start of problems caused by local householders who objected to the project.
- May/June 1999 - Plans placed in local library with a sheet for signatures to gauge support for the project. There were 50 responses of which over 70% were anti.
- June 1999 - Community Council meeting attended by 50 members of the community, who mostly objected to the project.
- July 1999 - Sub-committee met to discuss the future of the project.
- Sept 1999 - Sub-committee announced its decision to drop the project.

The biggest **challenge** for the project unfortunately has been insurmountable. Following a leaflet drop about the Litter Pick-up in May 99, some of the residents of the houses bordering onto the woodland became aware for the first time of the precise location of the project. Many had known of the project before, but had thought that it might have been north or south of the site . A campaign of objection developed.

To address this sudden and unexpected development the sub-committee placed the project plans in the local library and asked for names to gauge the level of support for the project. Over 70% of 50 responses signed against the project. Following this, around 50 objectors attended a Community Council meeting arranged to discuss the project. The concerns of the objectors were on issues such as an increase in the already present problem of drinking, vandalism and fire-raising. In addition, access to private property, an increase in car parking and a devaluing of property values were cited, a typical 'Not In My Backyard' (NIMBY) response. Most of these arguments could have been put forward to support the project whose aim was to improve the area with more regular use and care given to the woodland!

The objectors also accused the Community Council of secrecy in developing the project. The meeting was attended by SWT representatives who then withdrew their recommendation for the Biffaward due to the lack of community support. The strength of the objectors' campaign resulted in a decision by the Community Council to drop the project. There has unfortunately been no solution to this obstacle at Capelrig Wood. There are, however, many lessons to be learnt.

Greatest achievements? Despite the ultimate failure of the project there was still a sense of achievement. The effect of the community pulling together at the two litter collection events was very satisfying for those who attended. For the children, the involvement with the design was very valuable. For the sub-committee there was a sense of pride that so many organisations were prepared to provide support and funding, indicating that it was a worthwhile project.

The fundraising was the most challenging aspect (leaving aside the problem of the objectors). It was undertaken by only one member of the sub-committee and was hard work and stressful. There was also a lack of confidence, by some of the sub-committee members, in the project succeeding in the face of the various demands imposed by funders. This resulted in an 'all or nothing' attitude to fundraising indicating that the project would be halted if the full amount was not secured. This may have contributed to the collapse of the project when little resistance was made to the objectors to the project. Some may have felt a sense of relief.

Sources of help and advice? There were some skills found to be useful within the sub-committee. Skills came from members' own occupations- one worked in large-scale project management, another was a business consultant and a third had accountancy skills. Sub-committee members also drew on contacts already known to them such as the local Horticultural Society and Community Service Volunteers to provide help with habitat surveys.

The process of planning and fundraising resulted in many valuable contacts. The Scottish Wildlife Trust local area office was helpful on many fronts- advice on path construction, costings and identifying the Biffaward scheme. The Forestry Commission Woodland Officer helped with developing a Woodland Grant Scheme application and would have gone on to help

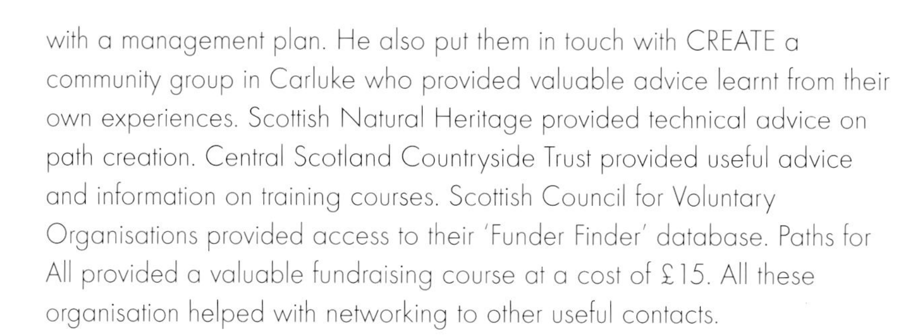

with a management plan. He also put them in touch with CREATE a community group in Carluke who provided valuable advice learnt from their own experiences. Scottish Natural Heritage provided technical advice on path creation. Central Scotland Countryside Trust provided useful advice and information on training courses. Scottish Council for Voluntary Organisations provided access to their 'Funder Finder' database. Paths for All provided a valuable fundraising course at a cost of £15. All these organisation helped with networking to other useful contacts.

The main funders potentially were; Mearns Community Council, Biffaward, New Deal, SNH, FC, Shell Better Britain, BT Countryside for All, NLCB Awards for All, East Renfrewshire Council (Small Environment Grant & Challenge Fund), Mearns Local Area Committee and ASDA.

Future activities? Unfortunately, at present, there does not seem to be the will to resuscitate any aspect of the Capelrig Nature Path project or to further any other community projects.

Lessons for others? Several factors may have contributed to the problem of the NIMBY reaction from the local residents. However, it is possible that nothing would have changed their attitude.

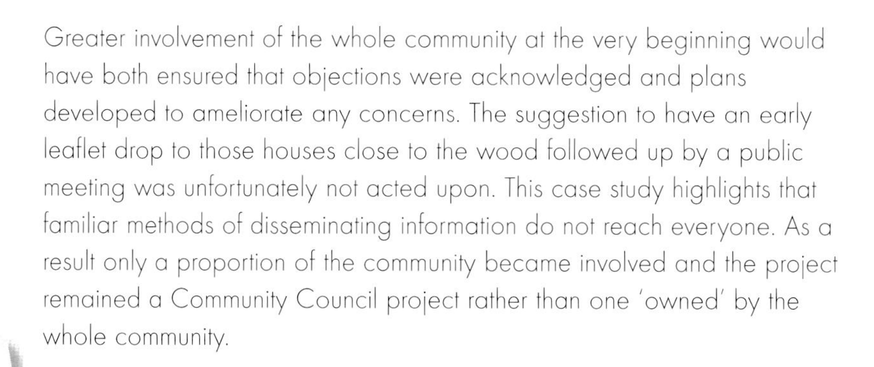

Greater involvement of the whole community at the very beginning would have both ensured that objections were acknowledged and plans developed to ameliorate any concerns. The suggestion to have an early leaflet drop to those houses close to the wood followed up by a public meeting was unfortunately not acted upon. This case study highlights that familiar methods of disseminating information do not reach everyone. As a result only a proportion of the community became involved and the project remained a Community Council project rather than one 'owned' by the whole community.

Contacts

Norie Mackie
Secretary

Capelrig Community Woodland
54 Caigton Drive, Newton Mearns
Glasgow G77 6TD

Email: norie.mackie@connectfree.co.uk

Enthusiasm for the project came mainly from one person who carried the others along. This worked up to a point, but when problems arose, such as the anxiety about funding, there was no core group of committed people to fight for the survival of the project or to share the worries. A group such as the Friends of Newton Mearns environmental group could have taken on this role, but the failure to get it established indicated a lack of community commitment to the area. As a result decisions were made by individuals while the community was left out, unaware of what was going on and disempowered from influencing the development of the project. Community spirit can be quite fragile.

Footnote

Community interest in the woodland has recently rekindled. In Feb 2001, Refreshing Scotland were invited to Capelrig, Newton Mearns, to carry out a participatory forest appraisal to determine community concerns and aspirations.

Newtonmore

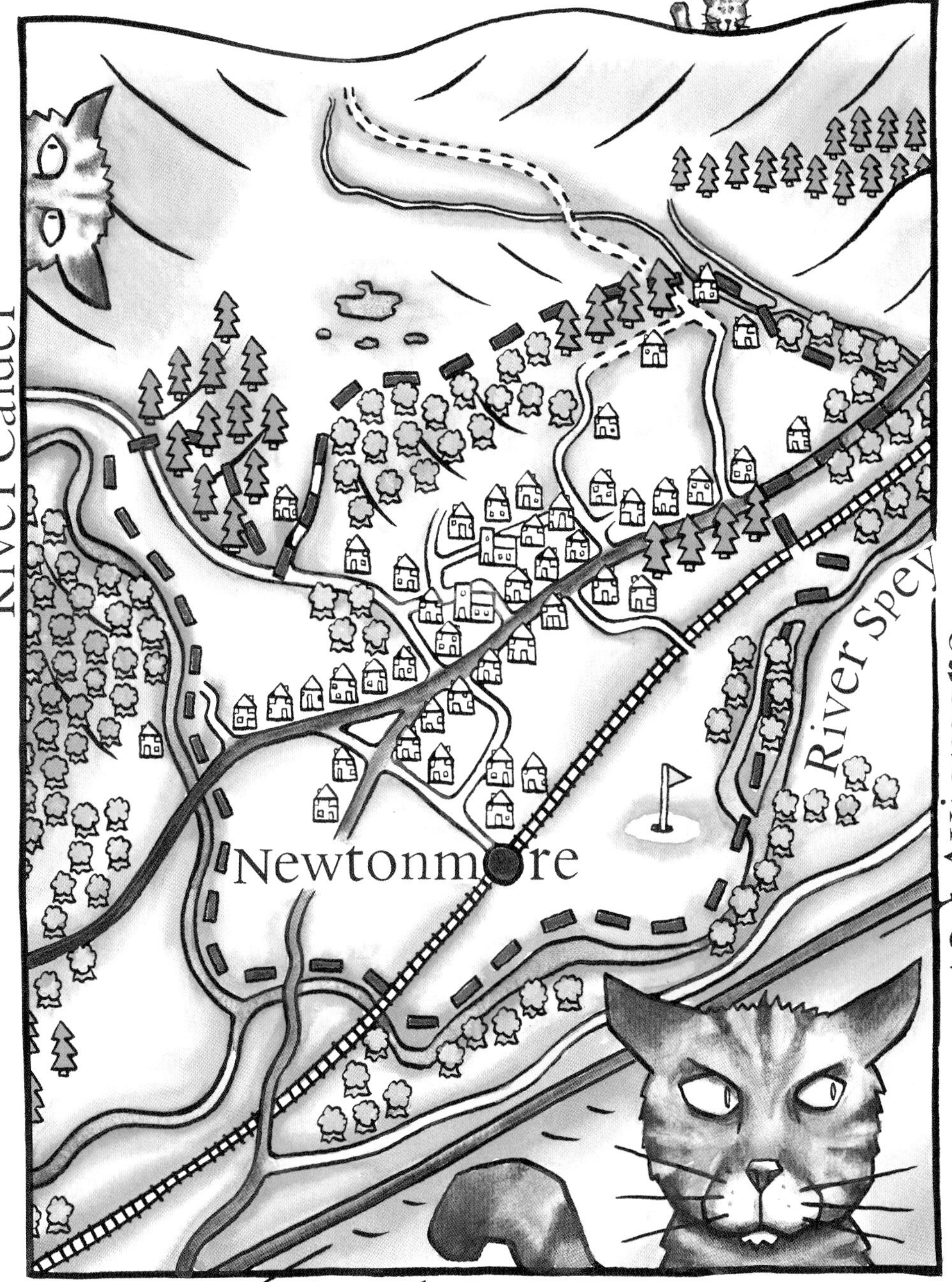

Summary

- Newtonmore Community Woodland surrounds Newtonmore village in Strathspey.
- The woodlands are varied, occupying 45 hectares linked by the Wildcat Trail.
- The woodlands are managed by agreement with the owners.
- Newtonmore Community Woodland Trust runs the project.
- The Trust is a Limited Liability Company with charitable status.
- The key aims are access to the natural heritage, shelter and tourism.
- The project was conceived in 1997.

Newtonmore

Why? A lovely area of pinewood near Newtonmore, in the central Highlands, was under threat from housing development. In fact Highland Council bought the site, but the pinewood was incorporated into the Highland Folk Park with entrance by ticket only. Highland Council was lobbied by the Newtonmore Community Council (NCC) to provide more access in the area. The village already has many excellent opportunities for short walks and is developing a reputation as a walking centre.

Then along came the Millennium Forest for Scotland Trust (MFST) in the shape of one of its promotion leaflets. MFST was looking for projects, the NCC was interested in the concept of community woodlands with good access and the funds on offer seemed too good to miss. The idea of linking old woods with new plantings was born. This developed into the **Wildcat Trail**. The wildcat was chosen to represent the walk as it has long been the symbol of Newtonmore and is on the crest of the Clan Chattan which includes such local names as Macpherson, Mackintosh, Davidson and MacBain. In addition, a rocky outcrop can be seen from the trail where a wildcat recently gave birth to a litter of kittens.

Who? The project is for the people of Newtonmore and the surrounding small communities as well as those who visit the area at weekends or on holiday. The community is easily defined as the catchment area for the local primary school. It is a cohesive community, the usual mixture of local families and incomers, all supporting the local services and the shinty team. The concept of walking for pleasure is not traditional, but this relatively recent activity is increasingly shared by everyone. Safe and interesting walking routes are also in great demand by visitors.

The NCC is long established and fairly representative of the community. As well as initiating the idea, the NCC will take back responsibility for maintaining the project in 2003. Meanwhile, it has set up Newtonmore Community Woodland Trust (NCWT) to run the project during its formative phase.

The Trust is a Limited Liability Company with charitable status and was formed in January 1998. Membership is open to residents of the Newtonmore area for an annual subscription of £1. There are 11 Directors/ Trustees of whom the Chairman, James Davidson, is responsible for coordinating the project and the Vice- Chairman, Dick Balharry, is responsible for interpretation. Other Directors have further responsibilities. An AGM is held every April with the usual election of Directors.

The NCC has 3 representatives on the Trust, one of whom is the chair of the community council. There is a Business Association in the village, representing mainly the tourist sector, which is also represented on the Trust.

What? The project consists of 45 hectares of woodland, in 16 compartments, around the village of Newtonmore, linked by a 10 kilometre orbital path known as the Wildcat Trail. This path can be walked as a single trail or accessed from various roads/ paths radiating out from the centre of the village. All of the land is owned privately or by Highland Council and so management is by agreement.

The Wildcat Trail is a spectacular walk which takes in native woodland, moorland, shelter belts, views of the Monadhliath and Cairngorm mountains and the river banks of the Spey and its tributaries, the Calder and Allt Laraidh. The trail passes through a Site of Special Scientific Interest (SSSI) and candidate Special Area of Conservation (cSAC) covering the Spey from Kingussie to the Spey Bridge upstream from Newtonmore, significant for its wildlife value, notably for salmon and otters.

The individual woodlands are very varied, giving a lot of interest to the trail. There is native woodland, dominated by silver birch, conifer plantations planted in the '60s, emerging natural regeneration and a few very old oaks (300 years +). There is also open ground, available for planting, some of which has already been planted up with native Scots pine and broadleaves. Some woodlands, such as the conifer plantations, lend themselves to management and are gradually being restructured, while others are difficult to access and will be left to develop naturally. Some of the riparian woodlands already have high nature conservation value.

In one of the shelterbelts the trees have been given to the village, while the estate retains the land or solum. This compartment will be gradually converted into a native woodland through removal of the introduced species. It is believed that some of the birch woodlands have arisen during previous periods when sheep stocking levels were lower, resulting in a pulse of regeneration. Such a pulse may occur again given the depression in the sheep industry.

The objectives for the woodlands are to enhance their amenity and conservation value.

Vision? The project revolves around access. The Wildcat Trail is the jewel in the crown of Newtonmore's bid to become known as the 'walking centre of Scotland'. There is a brochure describing the trail and a dozen other good walks in the area, all mapped and interpreted. The footpath network can be expanded and enhanced, especially if further land can be brought into the project. The various partner bodies and individuals will be monitoring the success of the Wildcat Trail with interest.

Ultimately, it is access to a high quality environment which is the vision. This both improves the quality of life of local people and brings in visitors who spend money and support jobs in the local economy. Tourism is the life blood of the area and a reputation for walking routes, in addition to the existing attractions, will encourage more people to visit and to stay longer.

The management objectives for the project are stated as:

- To increase the natural heritage value of the woodlands around Newtonmore
- To enable community involvement and encourage partnership
- To link with Laggan community in creating a major natural heritage asset

- To provide walks and a brochure for both residents and visitors
- To provide interpretation of the area
- To improve visual amenity and shelter
- To improve the area for crofting
- To develop a tree nursery

How? After making contact with MFST, a public meeting was convened by NCC in the village hall. The meeting was widely publicised and well attended with much discussion. As a result, the Newtonmore Community Woodland Trust was formed in January 1998. Various key people, including a professional naturalist, a farmer, a former head forester, a nurseryman, the clerks of both crofting townships affected and a solicitor, were approached and co-opted onto the Trust. Negotiations with landowners along the proposed route of the trail began. Some came on board quite quickly, others required more reassurance. The route had to be changed slightly to follow the line of least resistance. Access agreements were signed by July 1998. The owners have approved public access to the whole of the trail and to the woodlands by which it is linked.

The trail is marked by signposts and interpretative panels, while further information, disclaimers and requests for co-operation are contained within the brochure. The brochure is being distributed to all the tourist facilities in the village. Some, but not all, of the paths will be brought up to a standard suitable for people with a range of disabilities.

The **milestones** have been:

1. Conceiving the idea and convening the initial public meeting in 1997.
2. Setting up the Newtonmore Community Woodland Trust in January 1998.
3. Negotiating the route and initiating the project.
4. Completing the first phase of management works- fencing, footpath construction, signposting, planting, weeding and rabbit control.
5. Preparation of the Newtonmore- Walking Centre of Scotland brochure.
6. Inaugural walk on 1st January 2000 with a free dram and a certificate suitable for framing for those who completed the full route.

The biggest **challenges** have been:

- The competing uses of land for grazing, shooting, timber, cycling, golfing, quiet solitude and frenetic activity. The **solution** is to keep the dialogue open until an answer is found.
- The complexity of the grant system for busy people working on a voluntary basis. A possible **solution** would be to have a 'one stop shop' for grants. Ideally, every go-ahead community would have a staffed community office through which grants could be channelled directly to approved community projects, without each project having to do its own fundraising.

- The perception that SSSIs inhibit development of the land. The **solution** is to discuss projects early with SNH who can then advise on the possibilities for positive management.
- Problems with staff due to ill-health and other commitments. The **solution** to this is the same as elsewhere, to select staff carefully and replace them when necessary with others who can deliver the project's targets.
- The provision of road crossings and car parks. The **solution** was to discuss the issues, through the local councillor, with Highland Region and the Scottish Executive.
- The concern about being adequately protected against claims for injury. The **solution** has been to investigate and take out £2.5 million 3rd party liability cover with the NFU Mutual Insurance Co. Ideally the project would be covered under Highland Council's policy or that of some other organisation.

Greatest Achievements? One achievement has been the gathering together of the range of skills represented by the Directors. A good team has been built up and the project is meeting the targets it has set itself. Possibly the greatest achievement has been overcoming bureaucracy and the natural tendency of most people to procrastinate and obfuscate. The most challenging part has been getting agreement between so many owners and users.

Sources of help and advice? The skills of the Directors include woodland management, farming, crofting, conservation, interpretation, nursery practice, the law, skilled craftwork and organisational/ administrative skills. These latter included computer skills. When funding is limited, it is just as well that the Directors are so well qualified to run the project.

The practical work, including drawing panoramas for the signboards, is put out to tender. Local contractors are used when possible- most of the footpaths are being prepared by a local business. However, the timescale imposed by MFST has led to the planting and fencing being carried out by outside contractors with some loss of income to the local economy.

All the organisations the Trust has dealt with have been helpful, although each has its own perspectives and requirements, especially on timing. Personal contacts, for example with SNH, make a big difference in progressing issues smoothly.

The principal funders have been the Forestry Commission, through the Woodland Grant Scheme, and MFST. Additional amounts have come from SNH, Highland Council and Moray, Badenoch & Strathspey Enterprise Co. The funds have been raised with the usual effort. Further applications to trust funds are in process.

There has been little training to date. Two Directors attended the Reforesting Scotland Community Woodlands Conference in November 1999.

Future Activities? Current and planned activities are a continuation of the first phase with further fencing, planting, weeding, beating up and rabbit control. More footpath work is planned and 8 interpretative panels (5 at viewpoints and 3 in the village) are being erected. The car parking provision may be extended. The Trust is open to further opportunities for bringing woodlands and trails under community management.

The project is long-term and can easily be sustained at the current level of interest. As the Wildcat Trail becomes better known, there will be wear and tear and some further resources will be required to maintain it. There are some sleeping members of the Trust who are available to help if required. Any sign of enthusiasm quickly leads to an approach from a Director. The AGM provides an opportunity to formalise this process.

Lessons? The principal lesson is that quality is paramount. A community project should lead to community pride in that project. The quality should be higher than for any comparable project in the area.

It would have been very helpful if, in the early stages, someone could have met the Trust and talked about the experiences of other rural development forestry groups. The case studies will partially meet this need, but aren't as good as a person who can answer specific questions.

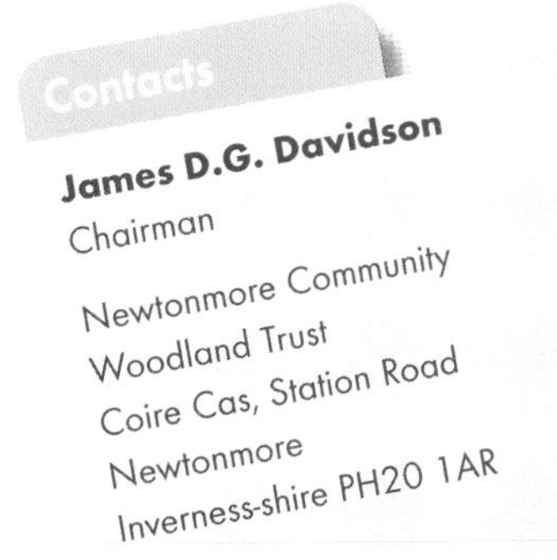

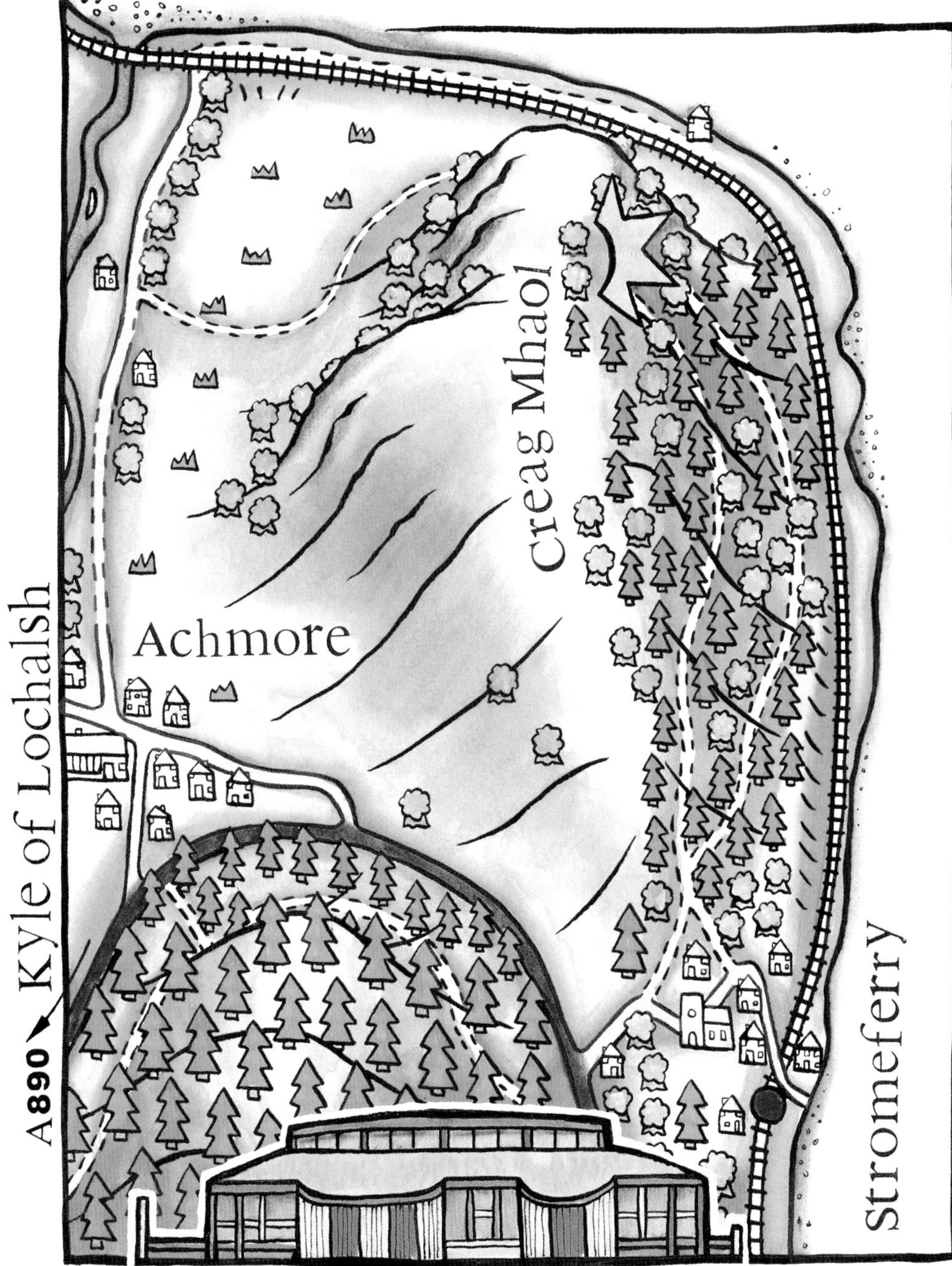

Summary

- Strome Wood is on the south side of Loch Carron, next to Stromeferry in Wester Ross.
- The wood is 30 hectares of mainly conifers of mixed age on steep ground.
- Management is likely to be by partnership with Forest Enterprise.
- Fernaig Community Trust is the community organisation developing the project.
- The Trust is a company limited by guarantee.
- The key aim is to revitalise the community.
- Discussions started in 1996.

Strome

Why? Achmore village is largely a Forestry Commission village, built in the 1950s. While the village is still surrounded by forest and woodland, the only forestry related jobs left in the immediate area are those of two stalkers, who between them cover most of Wester Ross. Most of the people living in the village and surroundings have past forestry experience.

Achmore has an unusually high percentage of children and there is concern about local employment opportunities for them in the future. The local school closed about 15 years ago, there are no longer any pubs, hotels or shops (although there is a railway station at Stromeferry) and the village hall has fallen into disrepair. Some members of the community, who have an interest in land reform, decided that they wished to try and tackle the situation and find ways to help revitalize the community. They had heard of the Laggan project and this stimulated thinking about how the surrounding forest areas might again be used to bring more benefits to the community.

Who? The community in this instance is defined (in the Memorandum and Articles of Association of the Fernaig Community Trust) as those living within the Stromeferry Community Council boundary. It includes the two settlements of Stromeferry and Achmore. The project aims to benefit the whole of this community and others visiting the area.

The Strome Forest Initiative is one of the projects being taken forward by the Fernaig Community Trust, a Company Limited by Guarantee. The Trust has five directors who are elected by its members. The annual subscription is £1, and the members own the Trust. There are currently 43 paid-up members out of a community of approximately 100 adults, and more are expected to join in the near future. The SFI project is run by a steering committee from the membership, 3 of whom are Trust directors. As with most small communities, there is a core of active people who are involved in most of the community initiatives, however, there is general support and interest in the project from the rest of the community.

There is no formal link between the Community Council and the Trust, although three Trust directors are Community Councilors. The Community Council is supportive of all the activities of the Trust and has contributed financially.

What? The original idea was to try and find a way in which the community could become involved in and benefit from the adjacent 1689ha (4,173acres) South Strome Forest owned by Forest Enterprise. After a series of discussions with Forest Enterprise about issues such as better opportunities for local contractors, the focus moved towards the development of tourist facilities.

Current ideas in terms of forestry are now focused on two main projects. One is the development of a shop and cafe with associated facilities. The other is the creation of recreational facilities in a nearby discrete area of the forest called Strome Wood, which is scheduled in the Forest Design Plan as a long term retention. This is not a production area for Forest Enterprise and so alternative management will not compromise the financial output of the forest. These ideas have had the support of and encouragement of Forest Enterprise and a partnership agreement is currently being discussed.

Strome Wood covers 30 ha (74 acres) of a steep craggy north facing slope with spectacular views over Loch Carron. It is adjacent to the road into the tiny village of South Strome with its railway station. What was mostly a Victorian plantation, probably felled during the first World War, was bought by the Forestry Commission in the 1920s. They replanted in the '20s and some planting was also undertaken in the 1970s. It now consists of an attractive mixture of mature Norway and Sitka spruce, western red cedar, larch and Scots pine with younger Sitka spruce and a little beech, birch, and hazel. There is some semi-natural birch and natural regeneration of many species in felled and cleared gaps, giving a fairly intimate mixture of species and ages. Signposted footpaths which were created by the Forestry Commission are now for the most part lost in the undergrowth and one or two clearings have been created by windthrow. There are stands of valuable timber which would present extraction difficulties due to the steep slopes.

Some ideas for the management of Strome Wood have been sketched out and are currently being costed. The general consensus is that the woodland should be managed primarily for amenity both for tourists and the locals. It should aim to provide some local employment through local processing, training opportunities and maximum community involvement. It is intended that the facilities will also attract visitors who will subsequently use the shop and cafe.

The ideas for the woodland include: reinstating and expanding the footpath network, opening up viewpoints, providing a small shelter/seat at the main viewpoint with information, thinning and pruning together with shrub and tree planting to create an informal woodland garden. They also hope to add a small car park and a direct footpath to the village.

A focus for the wider initiative for Strome Wood is a proposed roadside café and shop which will have a forest theme with woodland, historical, landscape and wildlife interpretation. The chosen site is a small patch of Forest Enterprise land beside a key viewpoint on the main road overlooking Stromeferry and the forest. The Trust wishes to purchase or lease the land from Forest Enterprise and run it as a wholly community owned facility. They would like it to be an innovative timber building, with an associated forest adventure playground which would provide a major attraction and stopping off point for passing tourists. It would act as a centre for forest trails and forest recreational activities as well as providing general information on the history and environment of the area. Forest Enterprise is very supportive of

this idea and is helping to further its development. It is hoped to develop links between South Strome Forest and the centre in terms of materials, crafts and information.

Vision? The overriding vision of the Trust is to develop projects which will bring local economic benefits and opportunities. At the same time it wishes to improve the local environment through real local involvement and generally promote a more sustainable future for the local community. Community participation in decision making and management will be crucial to this.

How? The sequence of events to date has been as follows:

- An initial approach was made to Forest Enterprise in 1996 about the possibility of the community purchasing the local forest. While Forest Enterprise was happy to enter into discussions, it fairly soon became apparent that this was not a practical possibility. Partly because of this and partly due to the fact that the community's ideas were changing and developing, discussions moved on to the development of a partnership between Forest Enterprise and the community to take their ideas forward.
- After about a year of discussing ideas, Forest Enterprise requested that in order for them to be able to take things forward there should be a properly constituted body. It also wished to ensure that the people with whom they had been holding discussions were sufficiently representative of the community and had community backing. During this period the same group of people were also attempting to purchase a large local estate (Fernaig) which had come onto the market and the Fernaig Community Trust was formed as a legal entity to take this forward.

- In the event the Fernaig bid was not successful though the Trust is currently negotiating the purchase of 82 acres of arable land for the community from the purchaser. However, it was decided to use the Trust, being representative of the community, as the constituted body for negotiations with Forest Enterprise. So, the Fernaig Trust is now negotiating with FE on behalf of the community and will be the body with whom the partnership agreement will be established.
- A draft partnership agreement for Strome Wood is currently under discussion between the Trust and FE. Once this is agreed, a management plan will be jointly drawn up and management tasks allocated. While several members of the community have forestry skills and already own chainsaws, it is expected that some training and certification will be required to allow them to work in the wood and to comply with health and safety regulations.
- Forest Enterprise is also interested in working in partnership with the Trust on the development of the cafe/shop/interpretation centre. It will probably supply timber for the building and general advice and assistance. The land will be either leased or purchased by the Trust. At present the Trust is discussing the proposals with the local planning authority and the local enterprise company. If responses

are favourable and grants are available, the project will be developed in greater detail with Forest Enterprise. Outline design plans have already been drawn up by a member of the Trust, who is an architect, for a timber built turf-roofed building.

The main **challenges** have been the restricted amount of time that Forest Enterprise and Trust members have been able to put into the initiative. All involved have jobs and other commitments. This means that progress has been a little slow at times.

However, this is not seen by the Trust as a serious problem and during this period there has been growing commitment and enthusiasm on the part of FE and members of the community.

Two of the principle turning points were the first site visit with FE, who as a result became enthused by the possibilities of the project, and the purchase of the arable land. This has demonstrated to the community what can be achieved.

The community has also been involved in a successful lottery bid for refurbishment and enlargement of the village hall at Achmore. The monthly community newsletter keeps the whole community informed about the various initiatives. There have been a number of community meetings at which the woodland has been discussed together with the other initiatives.

Sources of help and advice ? There are many Trust members with forestry experience and training and they are conversant with the structure and staff of the local Forest Enterprise District. The group feels that most of the skills needed are available within the Trust (architecture, planning, forestry, etc.) with the possible exception of law and administration. They are undoubtedly envious of Laggan's full time paid secretary and are currently looking into funding for a full-time administrator or project manager.

Apart from the close relationship with FE which has promised to supply as much help as possible in materials and expertise (while the Trust can hopefully access funding not available to FE and supply voluntary labour), the other official organisations with whom they have been in contact to date are the HIE Community Land Unit and the Local Enterprise Company. The group feels that it has had very valuable and generous advice from Laggan, Abriachan, Cairnhead and other community woodland groups which it has contacted.

No other potential sources of funding have been pursued to date as the group recognises the need for plans, proposals and agreements to be made more concrete before applications can be made.

Future activities? There is now sufficient community enthusiasm for the project for the momentum to be sustained even if some of the prime movers were to drop out. Older members of the community are becoming more enthused and will no doubt provide further expertise and help. When the time comes to produce a management plan for the woodland, this may be undertaken through a structured exercise such as Forests for Real. There are

Contacts

Colin Parsons

Fernaig Community Trust
6 The Square, Achmore
Stromeferry, Ross-shire IV53 8UN

already good lines of communication within the community and most of the key issues have already been tackled through discussions.

Lessons for others? As this project is still in its early stages there are undoubtedly many lessons to be learned, but two key ones are:

- the value of networking and seeking advice from other initiatives
- the value of maintaining a clear dialogue with potential partners and with the wider community.

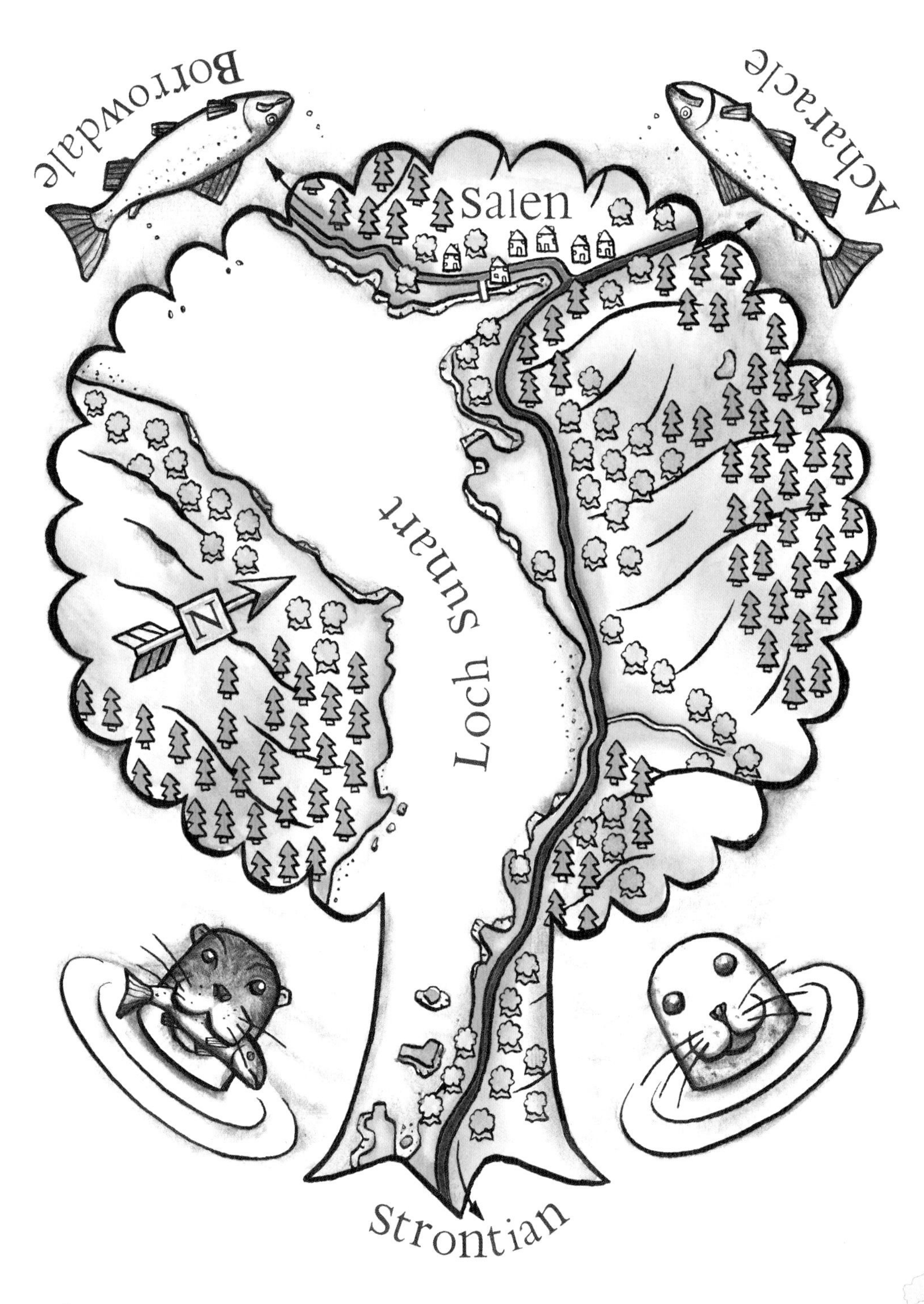

Summary

- The Sunart Oakwood Project is on the south side of the Ardnamurchan peninsula.
- The project area extends to 1318 hectares. It is 70% conifer, 19% native broadleaves and 11% open ground.
- The woodland is managed by a partnership of the local community, Forest Enterprise and others.
- The Steering Group of the partnership directs the project.
- The partnership is informal and unconstituted.
- The key aims are to restore the Atlantic oakwood habitat, to manage the woodland sustainably to support the local economy and to learn about the woodland's biodiversity and history.
- The idea had its origin in 1994.

Sunart

Why? The idea for the project originated in 1994 when Forest Enterprise (FE) consulted the local community on plans to restore an ancient oak woodland at Sunart on the Ardnamurchan peninsula. There was a strong desire within the community to create local employment. This is a community which understands forestry, in fact many older members of the community had been involved in planting some of the early plantations. Training in forestry skills was seen as a way to encourage the development of new businesses. Restoration and employment became the principal foci of the project. In addition, the community was keen to develop greater participation by the local primary schools in the forest.

The project has been characterised from the outset by a positive attitude within both FE and the community towards a partnership approach. This has enabled new opportunities to emerge. FE and the community have been joined by several other agencies and interest groups. Together, this has evolved into the Sunart Oakwoods Project.

Who? The local community is based around the villages of Glenborrodale, Salen, Strontian and Acharacle on the Ardnamurchan peninsula. This is an economically fragile area which has been identified as a pilot site for the European funded 'Initiative at the Edge'. Gaelic is spoken throughout the area which has a rich cultural identity. The main sources of employment are tourism, fish farming, agriculture (crofting), game shooting and public services.

The Acharacle Community Council (ACC), which provides the focus for local involvement in the partnership, serves a resident population of around 800, rising in summer as the large number of holiday properties become occupied. Help from the Initiative at the Edge steering group has provided a mechanism for wider community contact, through regular public meetings. This has speeded up the development of the project.

The ACC discusses the project at its monthly (open) meetings and exchanges ideas between local people and the partnership. Information is passed on via monthly newsletters, the local press and display boards as well as by word of mouth. Minutes of meetings are posted in the local libraries. Information days are held every six weeks to provide training and information on topics of special interest. These may take the form of group visits or lectures by guest speakers. Events are held which attract different groups within the local community and visitors to the area.

The partnership has developed in a very informal way. The main partners are the local community represented by ACC, FE, local landowners, SNH, Highland Council and the Local Enterprise Company. Several of the funding bodies are included in the partnership. Other interest groups are involved as appropriate, sometimes on sub-groups.

There is no constituted structure such as a trust. The Steering Group oversees the whole project and is chaired by John Risby from FE. This group directs the development of the project, identifies future funding possibilities and coordinates sub-groups, such as the Deer Group, Skills and Training Group and Archaeology Group. The Steering Group also directs the work of the recently appointed Project Manager, Jamie McIntyre.

What? The woodland is made up of Atlantic oakwood, open ground and planted conifers. Its location is between Glenborrodale and Strontian on the northern shores of Loch Sunart, which separates the Ardnamurchan and Morven peninsulas on the west coast of Scotland. The FE woodland area is 732 ha consisting of 70% conifers, 19% native broadleaves and 11% open ground. This is managed in conjunction with a further 586 ha of privately owned native woodland and open ground. Much of the native woodland is dominated by sessile oak which was worked for coppice nearly 200 years ago. The secondary species is downy birch with alder, ash, Wych elm, rowan, holly, willow, hazel and Bird cherry also present.

The flora is particularly rich in epiphytes and this together with the presence of otter habitats has resulted in the site being designated as an SSSI and a cSAC. The site is an ancient woodland which had been managed in the past for charcoal production and more latterly as crofting land until acquired by the Forestry Commission (FC) in 1951. The FC undertook considerable conifer planting throughout the oakwood between 1951 and 1971.

The original objective for the woodland was to restore the oakwood by removing conifers and rhododendrons. To this has been added the objectives of maximising local benefit and providing access for multiple uses.

Vision? The vision has three elements. Firstly, to restore the Atlantic oakwood habitat. Secondly, to manage the woodland sustainably to support the local economy. Thirdly, to give access to the woodland to learn about its biodiversity and history.

These objectives are listed as:

- Restoration of the Atlantic oakwood habitat.
- Training for local people in forestry and land management.
- Support new business enterprises for wood products.
- Involvement of schools.
- Develop access to woodlands for the interpretation of natural and cultural history.

How? The project began in 1994 with the consultation by FE on restoration plans for the oak woodland. During this process the local community clearly stated its interest in being involved, as there was a serious need for local employment. There had been little management activity by FE in the project area for quite a while and therefore little previous discussion with the community on management issues. Several open meetings enabled local people to become engaged and ideas to come forward.

FE developed a funding package and produced a management plan. Through the partnership, the community has shaped the Forest Design Plan through consultation and a Planning for Real exercise; initiated local training and employment; set out a framework for school activity and developed a Millennium Awards project to research the history of the woodlands.

The project has expanded, taking on a wider rural development role, by being incorporated into the Initiative at the Edge project. The emphasis is now moving from the initial aims of providing direct employment alongside the restoration of the woodland, to other uses of the diverse woodland resource and tourism.

It was also recognised early on that knowledge and understanding of the local woodland by all age groups was important to ensure that the woodland resources are managed sustainably and for the greatest benefit of the community. Of particular importance is the involvement of the four primary schools in the area. Initial involvement began with informal guided walks and class work on the wildlife and history of the woodlands. School children have been encouraged to express their views on the future management of the woods, such as providing ideas on the designs for car parks and interpretation facilities. There is a Gaelic Medium Unit within Acharacle Primary School which is exploring the cultural aspects of the woodland's history.

A Project Manager has recently been appointed to take the rural development aspects of the project forward. He has been appointed by FE on behalf of the partnership. His main responsibilities will be to ensure sustainable management and to increase community involvement by encouraging local use of timber, working with crofters to expand the woodland area and co-ordinating the various aspects of the project.

The **milestones** have been:

1. FE began to formulate restoration plans in 1994.
2. Securing MFST (1996) and LIFE (1997) funding for restoration work.
3. First school visit to see horse logging in 1997.
4. Preparing and receiving endorsement of a management plan in 1998.
5. First 4 local men trained as chainsaw operators in 1998.
6. Launch of Initiative at the Edge and incorporation of the Sunart project into this wider rural development initiative in 1998.
7. Securing Leader II funding for recreation and interpretation development in 1999.
8. Completing management agreements with 6 neighbouring landowners and formation of Deer Control Group in 1999.
9. Securing Rural Challenge funding for the Acharacle training and skills development project in 1999.
10. Support for the Moidart Horseloggers.

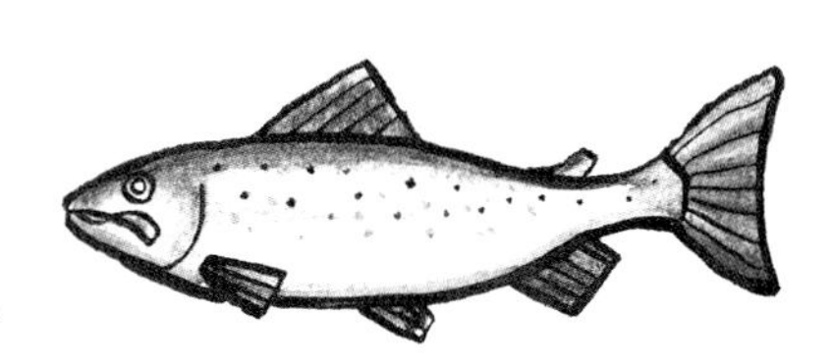

11. Appointment of the Project Manager in 1999.
12. Investigation of oak sawmilling in Ardnamurchan.
13. Development of a Millennium Awards project in 1999 to research the archaeology and history of the woodlands.
14. Development of forest walks.
15. An area of forest next to Acharacle Primary School was handed over in 1999 to the community by the local estate as a Millennium gift.
16. A Training and Skills Coordinator was appointed in November 1999.

The project has evolved in an informal way and there have been no great obstacles to overcome. The only problem of note has concerned the extraction of timber from an area covered by a nature conservation designation. This situation is being discussed with SNH in order to find a solution which suits everybody.

Greatest achievements? The greatest achievement has been seeing the tangible results already coming from the project outlined in the milestones above. This demonstrates that there are many real benefits for the local community.

The most challenging aspects have been securing funding and developing effective two-way communication. On the whole securing funding has not been too arduous as several of the agencies in the partnership have provided funding or have made the funding applications. As time has gone on the funding has become very complex. The most difficult funding to secure has been for access, interpretation, training and facilitating community involvement. This has been helped by raising the public profile of the project and through becoming involved with Initiative at the Edge. Effective communication has resulted from the agencies listening to the community.

Sources of help and advice? Most of the skills required have been accessed from within the partnership. There has been no need to look further afield largely due to the diverse range of agencies and individuals involved. The profile of the project has been raised by linking up with other initiatives.

To date the main funders have been FE, MFST, LIFE, LEADER II, SNH, Highland Council, FC, Crofters Commission, Lochaber Ltd. and the Rural Challenge Fund.

Training needs were identified early on and courses have been established. Many people already had the skills, but needed to be covered by certification to be employed. The provision of training has been demand lead. So far about 20 people have received training in areas such as chainsaws, pesticides and fencing. This has enabled them to set up as self-employed contractors. Future training will include the development of final products. The training of local people has coincided with the restoration of the woodland. This is ongoing and provides steady work such as the cutting of conifers and rhododendrons and the control of grazing.

Future activities? Ongoing activities include the training programme for forestry and land use skills, a series of school visits and practical activities, the development of access and interpretation facilities and the involvement of the wider community.

There are plans for a Forest School building, to be build from local timber and designed as a focal point for education within the woodland. Appropriately designed chalets, again built out of local timber, will increase the attractiveness of the area for tourists. As the project evolves, new ideas are developing and different groups of people are becoming involved.

Lessons for others? The most important lesson has been the value of a positive attitude towards working together, by all groups involved. This has been facilitated by wide consultation and general discussion so that as many people as possible in the community have had the opportunity to be aware of developments and to become involved. As a result the full benefit to the whole community is being realised.

Contacts

Sheila Nairn
Chairperson

Acharacle Community Council
Kentra, Acharacle PH36 4LA

Email: sheila@kentra.fsnet.co.uk

Summary

- Tinker's Bubble is in Somerset, to the west of Yeovil.
- The site occupies 16 hectares, half conifer plantation, the rest broadleaved woodland, orchards, gardens and meadows.
- The land is owned by a cooperative.
- The Tinker's Bubble Trust owns the woodland with the resident group making many of the day to day decisions.
- The landowning co-operative is a trust.
- The key aim is to provide a place for people to work and derive a living from the land, "organically, sustainably and collectively".
- The project began in January 1994.

Tinker's Bubble

Why? A small group of friends, living in the south of England, found they shared a common passion for working in woodlands or on the land. Each had, for some time, been looking for his own piece of land to rent or buy. It was discovered that Norton Covert (the name of the 16 hectare woodland now known as Tinker's Bubble), near Yeovil in Somerset, was on the market. While it seemed an ideal site, it was larger than any of them had been considering and beyond any of their individual means. Therefore, the obvious approach was to consider some kind of co-operative purchase. In fact one individual invested a significant proportion of the total capital required.

The principal aim at the time was to gain access to woodland that could be worked. Individual dreams or visions were not identical at the outset, although most shared a common outlook, having met through road protests and similar initiatives.

Who? The project benefits the Tinker's Bubble shareholders and residents, although there are widening connections and benefits to others.

The land is held by a co-operative of shareholders (currently 15). These comprise the original purchasers plus a few others who have bought into the co-operative. Not all of the shareholders live on the site. There are currently three women, eight men and four children living and working on the site. Not all of these are shareholders.

All decisions about the project are made collectively at monthly meetings in which all participate. On the very rare occasions where there is any dispute, the fully paid up shareholders – i.e. the landholding co-operative - have the power of arbitration or veto. There are also weekly Monday morning meetings where practical decisions are made and tasks allocated.

Each member works on the infrastructure and necessary common works for two days per week. The remaining days (usually 5!) they work in their own areas on their own projects. There is a target of £9000 pa revenue from timber which is currently achievable, but which may not be sustainable once the current thinning regime is over, unless the group can add value on site.

Tinker's Bubble is adjacent to a local authority owned country park- Ham Hill, which has public footpaths crossing it and is open to the public. As yet there has been no formal relationship with the local community of Stoke sub Hamden, but there have been visits from and demonstrations in the local primary and secondary schools. The relationship with the village is growing steadily.

What? The south facing site covers 16 hectares of which 11 are wooded. The remaining 5 ha are orchards, gardens and meadows. The woodland consists of 8 ha of conifers, mainly larch and Douglas fir planted in 1960. The rest is a mixture of broadleaves- ash, sycamore, old hazel coppice, beech and two small stands of hornbeam. Part of the site is a County Wildlife Site and part of the woodland has been identified as ancient and semi-natural. Since planting there has been little or no management of the conifers and the main tasks are thinning and replanting with selective clearance of significant areas of laurel undergrowth.

Since its inception there has been a policy that no fossil fuels should be used on the site, nor should there be any use of mains electricity. All work is therefore undertaken manually and with the help of a gentle Shire horse and a wood driven steam engine, which powers a 20ft long sawbench, housed in a strawbale barn. Targets are therefore achieved fairly slowly.

Some members consider that it might have been better to do some of the basic work needed with machinery before moving in and establishing the non- fossil fuel rule. The possibility of a brief relaxation so that the tough hazel stools can be tackled with a chainsaw, has been considered.

The woodland is being managed under a system of group selection to provide a continuous cover mixed woodland with approximately 50% broadleaves and 50% conifers (revised from 100% broadleaves). There is a policy that no trees should be felled until there is a market or clearly defined purpose for them.

The main objective for the woodland is to introduce species and an age structure that will be most beneficial to the needs of the community and to wildlife. The proportion of the conifers will be slightly reduced. Young transplants, from a local supplier or growing wild in the wrong place, are being planted in groups in small clearings. Most groups are a mixture of broadleaves and conifers. Felled timber is used for planking, fencing and building construction. Surplus timber is sold and there has been no problem finding buyers.

The site also houses 3 goats, a loaned cow, some pigs, a cider press, various timber-built workshop buildings, residential 'benders', a communal roundhouse and a kitchen. Three photovoltaic panels and a small windmill together supply enough electricity for lighting, a small fridge and electric fences.

Vision? The vision for the project is of a place for people who want to work and derive a living from the land, "organically, sustainably and collectively".

The principal aims for the woodland are:

1. To manage the woodland sustainably without ecological deterioration; and to enhance its biodiversity

2. To provide a constant source of useful and potentially saleable timber, and a source of employment.

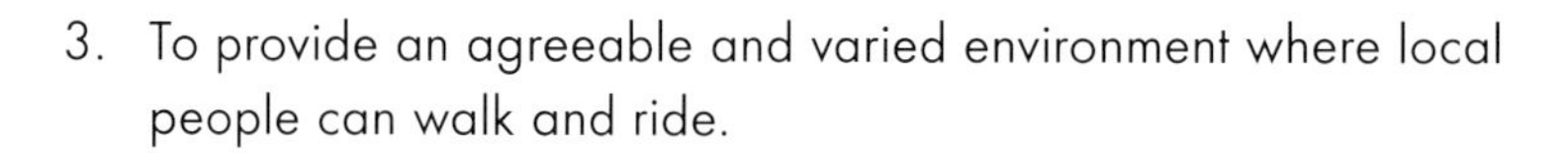

3. To provide an agreeable and varied environment where local people can walk and ride.

4. To provide a safe and agreeable habitat for humans and animals.

5. To contribute towards a policy that will enable Britain to become more self sufficient in timber and less dependent on foreign sources of questionable sustainability.

There are no specific long-term objectives - the group is conscious that they are still in a gestation period and feeling their way forward within agreed principles rather than towards defined goals. There is a feeling that the various nebulous and sometimes conflicting 'dreams' with which the project first started are beginning to coalesce into a clearer common vision.

The group is very much aware that the structure of the community and the development of common goals is an essential foundation of sustainability. One specific aim is that within 5 years each resident should be receiving an income equivalent to Income Support from the project.

The project is also deliberately pushing at the boundaries of planning law. To this extent it is seen as an experiment and has received considerable media attention. Paddy Ashdown is a supporter of the Tinker's Bubble experiment "even though it clearly falls outside the accepted planning regulations". The group wishes to demonstrate the appropriateness and sustainability of low impact development i.e. development with 'low adverse environmental impact'. There is currently a planning limit of 12 residents (people staying longer than 28 days) in "easily dismantleable wooden structures". The group believes that this is in fact the most that the site can adequately support, at present.

Another planning issue which is crucial to this project (and relevant to other community woods) is being vigorously researched and pursued by one member of the group. It relates to the fact that they only have planning permission to saw their own timber. If they saw timber for their neighbours, which would make sense from the sustainability point of view, it could be classified as an industrial process. If they 'add value' by making craft products from their own timber, similar restrictions could apply. The broader issue of people wishing to live on the land on which they are working is also being researched.

How? The project started off as a woodland owned by a small collection of people with similar skills and interests. In the early years of the project the focus was on the management of the woodland and the production of revenue from timber products. However, it became apparent that consolidation of the basic infrastructure- the living conditions and personal relationships, was crucial to the sustainability of the project and this is the main focus at present.

In terms of the organic vegetables, apples, juice and cider, production has been growing fairly steadily and the building of an earth roofed timber building to house the cider press has been an important milestone. Timber production has not been so smooth. At the beginning of the project a wood powered engine was set up in a field near the road and in the first month enough timber was sawn on the attached 20ft saw-bench for the group's needs for the first year, plus a significant injection of income through sales.

Undoubtedly one of the biggest **challenges** the project has had to face has been the subsequent enforced shutting down of the machine for two years due to a neighbour's objection to its noise. This has led to a long battle involving an appeal against the noise abatement notice and two planning applications.

Permission to use the machine in the new straw-bale barn (granted August1999) was therefore another significant milestone. However, the barn cannot be used for other activities such as crafts or courses. This has restricted the development of the group's plans. On the positive side, relationships with the local planning authority and the Forestry Commission are slowly strengthening.

Greatest achievements? The site in its current condition is testimony to the enormous number of man hours which have been expended. The greatest challenges have been the amount of work required from members (with few days off), the consolidation of goals and the development of the site infrastructure.

One problem the community faces is people who want to come and live on the site for short periods of time without making any contribution to the physical work. Various people, who were originally involved, have now left and there seems to be more stability within the core group.

Sources of help and advice? One of the non-resident shareholders has professional forestry skills, one resident has agricultural qualifications and another horse management skills. By and large, each person is steadily acquiring the necessary skills as the project evolves. There has been help and advice from the Forestry Commission, from the National Small Woods Association of which they are members, from the Soil Association and from the Horse Logging Association (now subsumed into FCA). No one has received any specific training since the onset of the project.

WWOOFers (Working Weekends on Organic Farms) and BTCV groups put in volunteer time and the project is also part of a local LETS (Local Economic Trading Scheme).

Income comes from a WGS management grant, a small grant from the Soil Association and sales of timber, organic vegetables, apples, apple juice and cider. Living costs for each member are £17 per week - wages are £3 per hour. Because living costs and therefore labour are so cheap, the group can produce goods, such as larch shingles, competitively without the use of petrol powered machinery.

Future activities? The general intention is to develop slowly, the first main target being to bring the woodland into steady production (50m^3 per annum average). Subsequently, the plan is to develop opportunities for adding value to the timber and possibly to expand the site and timber production potential by acquiring some adjoining conifer woodland and grazing land.

The group would like to improve/replace the existing buildings. In the future, there could be a few more people and their own livestock.

There is no end point to the project- it is very much an evolving enterprise. It is felt that 10-12 people are currently optimal, but that the level of physical work would ideally be reduced. Initially inputs may have varied, but it seems that all currently involved are more or less similarly dedicated. The weekly Monday meetings are seen as key to sustaining commitment and ironing out problems and differences.

Lessons for Others? This project is probably at one extreme end of the spectrum of community involvement in woodlands. One of the main things that the group would like to demonstrate to others is "that it can be done" i.e. living off the land with minimal environmental impact and producing a sustainable revenue.

They believe that their main challenges have been agreeing goals "When you start something up ensure that you have a vision and a plan- not just a dream", and then implementing the goals once they have been agreed.

There has been a long gestation period "It takes time to iron out all the wrinkles" and quite a time to overcome local negative attitudes to the people and project.

Finally, again from Paddy Ashdown, "after two or three years the outcome has been to add to not diminish the quality of life in our village. We have had to cope with different life-styles and different ways of looking at our world."

Contacts

Simon Fairlie
Tinker's Bubble
Stoke Sub Hamdon
Yeovil, Somerset TA14 6TE

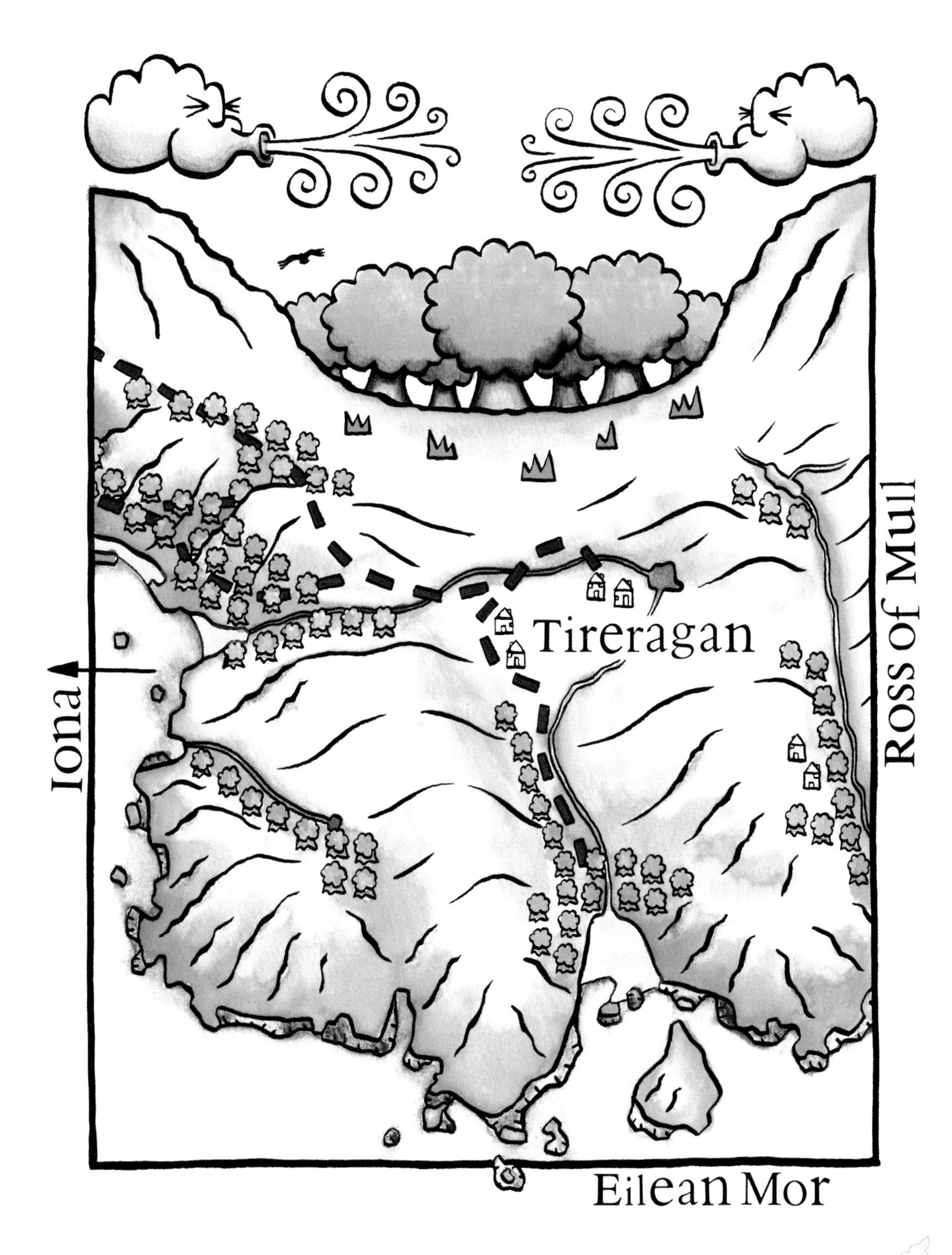

Summary

- Tireragan is at the very southwest tip of the Isle of Mull, Argyll.
- The land extends to 617 hectares of wild rugged coast and low-lying hills, covered by bog, heather and remnant deciduous woodland.
- The land is leased (30 years initially) from the local estate.
- Highland Renewal, a local charity, runs the project.
- Highland Renewal is a limited company with charitable status started in 1993.
- The key aims are regeneration, conservation, education, research and amenity.
- The project began in 1993.

Tireragan

Why? The current project at Tireragan has developed from the original vision of Carol Riddell, who in early 1993 established Highland Renewal (HR) as a charity with the aim of holistic regeneration of the Highlands and Islands, encompassing habitation, agriculture and conservation. Although Tireragan was to be the site of the pilot project, it became clear that the area was not a suitable location for re-population due to difficulties of access. At the same time, the conservation importance of the land became clear especially in terms of the remnant woodlands and their associated flora and fauna. Therefore at the start of 1999 the directors of HR decided to concentrate on Tireragan as a project for conservation, education and amenity. There are nevertheless rural development benefits flowing from the project. Now that Tireragan has become an amenity resource for everyone living on or visiting Mull, most of the local community are happy with the current direction of the project.

Who? As an area that is now recognised to be of both national and international conservation importance, you could say that in its own small way Tireragan is a resource that is important for the whole country. For the local community on the Ross of Mull, Tireragan is becoming an amenity to be enjoyed by all. For the wider community of Mull it is providing an excellent educational resource for the schools. It has also attracted postgraduate field research students from Manchester Metropolitan University (MMU).

Highland Renewal is a limited company with charitable status and all the directors either live on Mull or have a close link with the island. All have input into the running of the project and all the Directors' Meetings can be attended by anyone in the community if they so wish. It has always been a primary concern of HR to involve the local community at every opportunity and local people are encouraged to become involved with the project at every level. Highland Renewal and the Tireragan project would not have reached this advanced stage without major impetus and work from the board of directors, project managers and members of the local community.

What? Tireragan comprises 617 hectares of coastal hill land characterised by wooded valleys, blanket bog and heather topped low-lying hills. An important factor influencing the natural history of Tireragan is the weather. Lying at the very southwestern tip of the Isle of Mull, the land is open and exposed to the Atlantic and is therefore wet, mild in temperature and extremely windy.

The woodlands are remnants that have only just survived through the several centuries of human influence and are similar in many ways to the Atlantic oak woodlands seen at several sites along the west coast of Scotland. Currently birch, willow and hazel dominate the woodlands at Tireragan. Only time will tell if, as the woodlands regenerate, oak will eventually become the dominant species. There are certainly a significant number of very old oak trees that have survived through the centuries. What is clear is that the lower plants of the Tireragan woodlands are an almost unique assemblage of both national and international conservation importance.

Before Tireragan was fenced to keep sheep and deer at bay, the surviving woodland was mainly clinging to rocky slopes and wet hillsides where grazing or burning was difficult or impossible. Since the fence was completed and large herbivores excluded, the regeneration has been nothing short of spectacular, with birch and willow flourishing beyond expectations.

The objectives for the future of the woodland probably fall into two phases. Firstly, the regeneration phase which is largely a question of time, plus the continued maintenance of the deer fence. The second phase will be the management of the woodland to protect the abundance and diversity of the lower plants. At this time it is a matter of conjecture as to when the second phase will start. The management of visitors to Tireragan will always need careful monitoring.

Vision? In the long term Tireragan will be maintained as a conservation area. It may be twenty or thirty years before the woodlands start to gain their full ascendancy.

During this time, as regeneration continues, the area will become an increasingly attractive visitor attraction. The provision of such a valuable amenity and educational resource for both the local and wider communities will always be important though it will not be allowed to become detrimental to the land itself.

As a conservation research opportunity Tireragan will provide important information about the regeneration process and how the flora and fauna change over time. Links with research establishments such as MMU will be maintained and encouraged. Reports have been written on the flora, archaeology, ornithology and regeneration at Tireragan all of which have, or will be, published on the HR web site.

Perhaps the most important objective for Tireragan will be as an educational resource aimed at every level and age of visitor. From pre-school groups through to university level and beyond it is an aim that all who visit Tireragan leave with a greater understanding of the natural environment around them. This will be the primary purpose of interpretation material due to be installed during 2000.

Although it is unlikely that the woodland at Tireragan will provide an opportunity for large-scale commercial wood production, it is really unknown at this stage what small-scale projects might be possible in another thirty years. Already, the project has generated a great deal of work in fencing, planting and project management, all of which contributes to the local economy.

How? Highland Renewal has leased the land for at least 30 years at virtually no cost from the Dutch landowners who bought the estate with the express intention of leasing it to HR. The next significant **milestone** was the erection of the deer fence, an unfortunate but necessary evil, and the removal of sheep and deer from

the land. Equally important in encouraging regeneration was halting the burning of the heathland (muirburn). The erection of the fencing was made possible though a Woodland Grant Scheme (WGS) for regeneration, plus 36 hectares of new planting. With the advantage of hindsight and the knowledge of the speed of regeneration, new planting was probably unnecessary. HR now needs to spend time and money on maintaining the planted area to ensure it meets WGS requirements. It is a lesson learned.

Since the redefinition of the Tireragan project as conservation driven, a very significant milestone in itself, the current partnership with the Millennium Forest for Scotland Trust, together with Scottish Natural Heritage (SNH) and several other funding sources, has been established. This partnership has helped not only financially, but has also helped to create a clear plan for the next ten years. This process was completed with the publication of the Tireragan Management Plan at the start of 2000 (available at £6.95 from Highland Renewal or as a download from the Highland Renewal web site).

It is clear now that the single greatest achievement was in gaining control of Tireragan. Even Carol Riddell, who started the project, will probably admit that she did not realise what a special piece of land it is. It is becoming more special with each passing day. The simplicity of the project at its most basic level i.e. to have an area of land and let nature take its course, is incredibly rewarding.

However, as with most community projects, the most challenging part has been to try and mesh the various viewpoints held by directors and members so that the project can advance. The simplification of the Tireragan project, with its redefined conservation aims, certainly does not meet the original vision of Highland Renewal in its entirety, but does meet some aspects of it. Once the major works at Tireragan are completed then perhaps HR will tackle other projects that are within its remit.

Sources of help and advice? Highland Renewal has been fortunate to have a broad base of skills amongst its directors and members most of which have been lent to the project at one time or another. Due recognition, therefore, must be given to Carol Riddell, who as the first project manager was the initial driving force behind HR. Louise Walsh who as project manager until this year, administered the MFST funding package that assures the project's future for the next five years. Paul Haworth, as Chairman of HR since its establishment, has provided a steadying influence that again has been vital to the successful continuation of the project.

The project is indebted to Ben and Alison Averis who have lent not only their expertise in botany to the project, but their wholehearted support as well. Glasgow University Archaeological Research Department provided the expertise for the 1999 archaeological survey. John Grieve of the Forestry Commission has always been there to lend advice and support when needed, as have many members of SNH. Numerous volunteers have given their time and energy to the project over the last seven years and as a small project with a small budget every contribution has been notable and appreciated.

The main funding sources over the course of the project have been and will be the Forestry Commission, the Millennium Forest for Scotland Trust and SNH. There have been numerous other sources of smaller amounts of funding from both organisations and individuals.

Future Activities? Amongst activities for the immediate future are the installation of interpretation at Tireragan and the continued expansion of the Highland Renewal web site. The year 2000 saw the start of the installation of completely new interpretative material at Tireragan encompassing trails, way markers, leaflets and displays. The Highland Renewal web site will provide an interpretive experience for all on the Internet as well as becoming a source of all research and other material produced during the Tireragan project.

Many of the main works at Tireragan will be complete by the end of 2000, but monitoring and management will continue on an annual basis. In the medium to long term, issues such as allowing grazing to increase and what to do when the fence reaches the end of its useful life will arise. The right management decisions will be made easier by the monitoring and research that will be undertaken every year.

Lessons for others? Perhaps the most important lesson which has been learnt during the course of the Tireragan project is that one should never underestimate the importance of the resource. Time is a great healer and in many situations an understated approach may be better than over-management.

Contacts

Trish Haworth

Highland Renewal, Ben Doran Cottage
Benessan, Isle of Mull, PA67 6DU
E-mail: trish@bendoran.dabsol.co.uk
Website:
www.highlandrenewal.ndo.co.uk

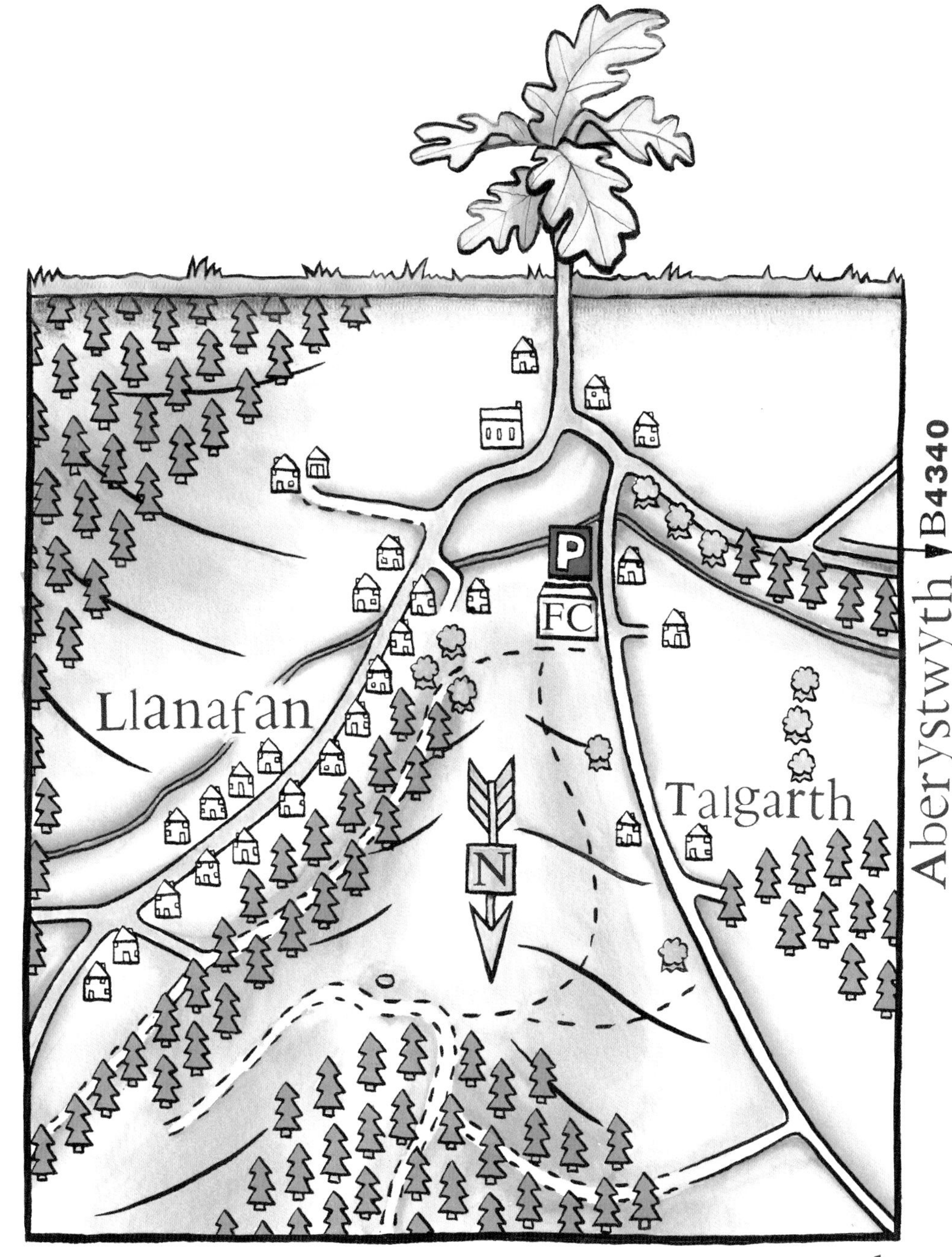

Trawsgoed

Summary

- Trawsgoed is located 10 miles up the River Ystwyth from Aberystwyth in mid-Wales.
- The focus of the project is the site of the old Forestry Commission office together with the extensive plantations in the area.
- Ideas on management are currently being developed.
- Cymdeithas Bro Trawsgoed Community Association (CBTCA) runs the project.
- CBTCA is a formal Community Association set up under the auspices of the Community Council. It has applied for charitable status.
- The prime objective of the project is to acquire a community asset and to develop awareness of the potential role woodlands can play in a changing rural economy.
- The project was initiated in 1998.

Trawsgoed

Why? The old Forestry Commission office (FC) at Llanafan, Trawsgoed near Aberystwyth in mid-Wales was closed due to relocation in 1998. The Forestry Commission had once been the major employer in the area with a tree nursery and several harvesting gangs, but over the years employment had dropped due to changing practices. The office became the focus for an exciting new community opportunity.

Forest Enterprise (FE) was granted outline planning permission for the construction of houses and the site was put onto the market for sale. Planning permission was opposed by Trawsgoed Community Council and a community association was formed, Cymdeithas Bro Trawsgoed Community Association (CBTCA), to try and find another use for the site. A questionnaire was distributed and a Participative Rural Appraisal (PRA) event held in November 1998 to explore potential sustainable uses for the site and the possibility of community ownership.

Who? The Trawsgoed community is defined by the Trawsgoed Community Council area and all those with an interest in the livelihood of the community living within close proximity. The main village is located 10 miles out of Aberystwyth. Most incomes are earned in town or out of the area. Changing agricultural practices mean fewer farmers and FE now only employs two individuals from the village. A number of retired forestry workers still live in the area and have strong associations with the surrounding forests. All the major employers have left the area over the last ten years with FC being the last to go. This provoked a strong reaction and with it came the realisation that conditions were no longer the same as they had been.

The community association (CBTCA) was formed by Phil Morgan under the auspices of the Trawsgoed Community Council with help from Ceredig Thomas and Ceridwen Lloyd-Morgan. Funding for a PRA was obtained through an Objective 4 grant and attention was drawn to the project at a meeting chaired by the local MP Cynog Dafis and facilitated by Antur Teifi of the LEADER Group. Numerous individuals have helped and participated in forming the Association.

A formal constitution was drawn up by a steering committee and the group was registered as a Community Association. The Association has a formal constitution and is now run by an elected committee. The Association is applying for charitable status and has applied for a Lottery Grant to assist in acquiring the site.

What? The site is not woodland, but an office site with a few exotic Eucalyptus trees around the periphery! The Community is seeking to acquire the site as a centre for training in rural diversification and to provide facilities for local business development.

The village is half way up the Ystwyth Valley in mid-Wales surrounded by very extensive areas of FE and privately owned plantation woodlands. The forest area at higher elevation is dominated by Sitka spruce, but the lower slopes and valley bottoms have a good mix of species. A very wide range of exotic species was planted in the 1950s in Wales in order to match species to site and to provide diversity. Fairly large areas were also established with broadleaves along roadsides, in particular with North American oak. A significant part of the housing stock in the village is old Forestry Commission houses with brick walls and shingle roofs giving the village a 'Commission' look and atmosphere. The village is at the transition between the lower coastal hills with their mixed woodland and pasture, and the bare uplands.

The prime objective of the project is to acquire a community asset and to develop awareness of the potential role woodlands can play in a changing rural economy.

Vision? Woodlands and farming, particularly with the current intensive management practices in both industries, have little direct value to the local economy. Very little value is added locally to the products of the countryside resulting in a lack of support for local communities which receive little benefit from much of the land around them. A further irony is that intensification is leading to environmental degradation so that communities see the natural assets around them disintegrating before their very eyes. The woodland initiatives in the Ystwyth area seek to explore local people's perceptions of woodlands, how they are used and how they might support the rural economy better. The vision of the project is to restore the links between local people and the countryside in a way which is appropriate to the 21st century.

The specific objectives of the project, in order of priority, are:

- To acquire the old FC office site at Llanafan.
- To develop the community asset as a training and rural development centre.
- To encourage local entrepreneurs and thus revitalise the local economy.
- To find alternative uses for woodland that support the local economy, both directly and indirectly, creating work through added value and multiplier effects.

How? A group of individuals opposed the FE planning application. They devised and circulated a questionnaire and presented the results at a specially convened community meeting.

The methodology and techniques of Participatory Rural Appraisal were introduced and successfully used to explore new possibilities. This enabled a wide range of ideas and opinion to be effectively considered including those from the younger generation.

The woodland site hasn't yet been acquired but, in the acquisition process, a far greater appreciation of woodlands and their effective contribution to the rural economy has been developing.

Two **milestones** to date have been:

- Participatory Rural Appraisal held in the local hall on 28 November 1998.
- Ystwyth Valley Forest Initiative hosted by Antur Teifi and chaired by Cynog Dafis MP, 8 January 1999.
- Tir Coed Ystwyth Valley Participative Rural Appraisal, September 1999. This was a very extensive valley wide initiative designed to gather views on possible woodland expansion in Wales.

The biggest **challenges** have been persuading FE to deal with the local community, finding funding for the project and encouraging agency support for rural community development.

The **solutions** have been awareness building, empowerment and the initiation of sustainable change catalysed through the use of PRA.

Greatest achievements? The initiative which has worked best for the group has been the Participatory Rural Appraisal exercises. This has built awareness and generated many good ideas for the future.

The greatest challenge has been in forming the Association and seeking wide community support.

Sources of help and advice? Within the group are individuals with local knowledge of organisations and agencies. They have had to have an awareness of changing circumstances. A great deal of commitment and personal time have been required. The main gap was in legal skills, which have been brought in from outside.

There have been many helpful people in a number of organisations. They include Cynog Dafis MP, Meinir Paske of the Antur Teifi LEADER Group, Roland Jones of Ceredigion District Council, Ceredig Thomas and Ceridwen Lloyd-Morgan of Trawsgoed Community Council, Aled Davies of the Welsh Development Agency and Ian Shaw of Forest Enterprise.

Very little funding has been required to date. Jigso provided a £250.00 grant to assist with forming the Association and drawing up a constitution.

The only training to date has been in PRA facilitation skills.

Future activities? Current efforts are going into various fundraising activities in order to achieve the project's principal aim.

There is no end point. The group could potentially grow to form a new institution, such as a Development Trust, that could become part of a wider network. Development Trusts require assets in order to enable communities to draw support and profit. In this case the assets are the surrounding woodlands which currently are non-viable as far as the community is concerned. Keeping the Association active and individuals motivated is achieved through mutual support.

Lessons for others? Although this is a very new project a few lessons have already emerged which the group would like to pass on to others.

- Use participatory methods at the earliest stage in dealings with the community.
- Make strong arguments to agencies for assistance towards sustainability.
- Consider networking with others to share ideas and to make efficiencies.

Contacts

Peter Gilbert

Cymdeithas Bro Trawsgoed Community Association
Penhiw, Llanafan
Aberystwyth, Ceredigion SY23 4BA

Summary

- Camusnagaul and Achaphubuil Woods are situated across Loch Linnhe from Fort William.
- They occupy 66 hectares, are predominantly broadleaved in character and are listed in the Ancient Woodland Inventory.
- They are owned by the local community.
- Treslaig and Achaphubuil Crofters Woodland Trust (TACWT) runs the project.
- TACWT is a company limited by shares.
- The key aims are to improve the ecological value of the woodlands and to increase their potential for local employment opportunities.
- The idea germinated in 1989 and came to fruition with purchase in 1994.

Treslaig

Why? The government announced in 1989 that the Forestry Commission (FC) would be required to dispose of some 100,000 hectares of land over a 10 year period. A Highland Councillor, Dr Michael Foxley, acting on behalf of a group of crofters living near Fort William, tried to register an interest in any FC plantations or land around their community which came up for disposal. He was treated 'with disdain'. This only made the community more determined to safeguard its interests and eventually it was successful in purchasing the woodlands.

Who? The project is for the benefit of the two crofting townships of Treslaig and Achaphubuil which are located opposite Corpach and Fort William across Loch Linnhe and connected to Fort William by a small ferry. There are eleven crofts at Treslaig and two at Achaphubuil. The FC land abutted directly onto the Treslaig common grazings and the Achaphubuil crofts and grazings.

Of the thirteen crofts, nine crofts (eight crofters) support the project, two crofters were very elderly widows and one crofter was an absentee.

After taking legal advice from Simon Fraser, who advised the Assynt crofters and Eigg islanders, a company limited by shares, known as the Treslaig and Achaphubuil Crofters Woodland Trust (TACWT) was established. This structure allows the shares to be sub-divided or amalgamated as the crofts pass on down the generations. There is a clause which requires 75% agreement to a share transfer. This is to ensure that the group remains as an effective co-operative. If somebody wishes to leave and the person to whom they wish to transfer their shares is not acceptable, then the company buys out that shareholding. The valuation is contained within the company structure so that it is a value placed upon a part share of the woodland and not the precise pro rata economic value of the shares. Another important point is that the company operates by one person/ one vote regardless of the extent of the holding.

What? The woodland is in two blocks known as Camusnagaul Wood (31.4 ha) and Achaphubuil Wood (34.2ha). Both are recorded on the Ancient Semi-natural Woodland Inventory. They have a north-easterly aspect and lie behind and between the two crofting townships. They form a significant part of the outlook from Fort William and the surrounding area.

The two woodlands have been surveyed and a management plan prepared. Taking Camusnagaul Wood, for example, the most common woodland National Vegetation Classification (NVC) types are:

- W4b Downy birch with purple moor grass (15ha)
- W17c Upland oak-birch with Dicranum moss (8ha)
- W11b Upland oak-birch with wood sorrel (4ha)
- W7 Alder ash with yellow pimpernel (3ha)

Most parts of the woodlands have the range of species associated with each of the NVC types, although the woods have been managed in the past and had other species introduced. The southern section of Camusnagaul Wood is the most artificial in species composition with large numbers of beech and sycamore. Most of the trees throughout are over-mature and natural regeneration is limited. This is due to the woodlands being grazed by sheep and small numbers of red and roe deer.

The history of the woodlands is interesting. There are signs of woodland dykes, thrown up in the past to protect stands from grazing during a regeneration period. These dykes were probably surmounted by woven hazel hurdles which lasted for the 5 or 6 years necessary for a pulse of natural regeneration to take place in the absence of grazing pressure. Pulses of regeneration of birch and mixed species have taken place at certain times in the past and can be seen. Oak stumps may be seen in some of the clearings and many of the oaks appear to have been coppiced in the past. The 'platform' areas may have been used for charcoal production or may be the sites of old croft houses. The woodland was managed by the MacLeans of Ardgour who owned the land up until 1833. From information arising from the Loch Shiel and Loch Sunart side, these woodlands would have been actively worked by coppicing and selective felling.

The area has extensive archaeological remains including dykes, lazy beds and hut circles. These have been surveyed.

The overall management objective is to maintain the woods at their present extent and ecological value. This is regarded as a minimal target and other objectives have been added:

- encourage tree and shrub regeneration
- extend the woods by regeneration or planting
- encourage native species
- discourage non-native species
- increase habitat diversity
- encourage, by habitat modification, threatened species such as the Chequered Skipper butterfly
- monitor habitat changes and target species

These objectives are stated and developed in the management plan prepared in 1997.

Vision? The long term vision is to ensure that the woodlands are safeguarded for future generations. The woodlands are in a fragile state in places with few oaks younger than 100 years.

By improving public access to the woodlands and encouraging people to travel over from Fort William to walk in the woods, the local ferry and other local enterprises will be supported.

Project management objectives, in addition to the woodland management objectives, are listed in the management plan as follows:

- encourage the potential of these woods for local employment opportunities
- encourage benign and sustainable exploitation of woodland products at a local scale
- integrate agricultural production and stock management as far as possible into management regimes developed to achieve the above objectives
- improve the woods for red deer in the long term
- encourage use in education and for public and community recreation
- preserve and protect from damage the archaeological and historical features of the site
- demonstrate to other landowners and land managers, the management and harnessing of the environmental, economic and other potentials of these woodlands

It is argued that jobs and training will develop in nature conservation management operations as well as through harvesting and processing the timber at an appropriate scale and timescale. A financial return to the local community is the best way to ensure that the woodland is conserved. It is further hoped that stock grazing can be used as a valuable management tool.

How? After the initial rebuttal by the FC Land Agent, the group explored the possibility of Sponsorship with the then Nature Conservancy Council. They were told that the group had to have a well established record of land management and nature conservation and that as a group of crofters, they didn't qualify. NGOs such as the RSPB and Scottish Wildlife Trust were held up as the sort of groups which could qualify for sponsorship. In fact, FC approached the Woodland Trust in 1991 to see if that organisation would be interested in purchasing the woodlands. Neither organisation consulted with the crofters or informed them that these discussions were going on. When the Woodland Trust inquired about local funding, it was told politely that any local funds would be available for the local community and not for an outside conservation interest.

In 1992, the FC informed the community that it was going to offer the woodlands back to the son of the original owner under the 'Crichel Down' arrangements despite the land having been freely sold in 1961. After intense political lobbying, a compromise was reached whereby the hill ground was offered back and the woodlands sold on the open market. Issues such as access, shooting rights and the valuation were clarified, TACWT was set up and the woodlands were finally bought by the community, sponsored by SNH, in 1994 for £15,000.

On the night of the entry date, Michael Foxley and the chairman of the group, Jimmy Morrison, drank a dram of whiskey to the memory of the chairman's great aunt who had been fined 2/6p for collecting firewood within the woodland.

The greatest **challenges** had been overcome. These were the arrogance or indifference displayed by the agencies to a local community. Little did they realise how the community would get stuck in or how the political atmosphere would change to support community initiatives, especially their 'right to buy'.

Greatest achievements? The greatest achievement has been succeeding in buying the woodlands. The most challenging part has been dealing with the negative attitudes of the FC land agents at that time.

Sources of help and advice? The group of crofters displayed enthusiasm and determination. They were supported by key individuals associated with land reform in the Highlands, including Jim Hunter, Duncan Grant, Bill Ritchie and Simon Fraser. Donald Kennedy of Organic Trees, surveyed the woodlands, produced the management plan and has given considerable advice to the group over several years. An MSc student from Edinburgh University, John Bryant, prepared an Interpretation Plan, developed the walking trails and produced a trail leaflet.

Jeff Watson and George Hogg of SNH advised the group and helped to develop the Sponsorship of the sale. SNH contributed 50% of the purchase price. Highland Regional Council and Lochaber LEADER were the other major contributors. An application has been made for landfill tax funding. Being a company limited by shares, the group isn't eligible for charitable status.

There has been no training to date.

Future activities? A WGS Woodland Improvement Grant (WIG) has been applied for and approved. This will help to pay for fencing and other operations. The planned management activities are:

1. The woodlands are to be fenced against deer and stock.

2. Within the fence, stock will be introduced in small numbers at selected times to increase biodiversity and to respace the birch regeneration, which is expected to explode.

3. The effects of the stock will be closely monitored.

4. There will be limited new planting, especially of less common species such as holly.

5. There will be selective thinning of the birch and selective felling of introduced species such as sycamore, beech and Sitka spruce.

6. The finest of the mature beech trees will be retained for their landscape and amenity value.

7. Bracken will be controlled over large areas by spraying and cutting.

8. Habitat management will benefit the rare butterflies found in the woodland.

9. The footpath system will be extended and made accessible to visitors.

The structure of the group with the possibility of passing shares down the generations or to like-minded individuals is expected to keep the project active and ensure continuity. The aim is to include future tenants of any of the crofts, if they wish to become involved.

Lessons for others? 'You have to fight and fight very very hard to establish community ownership against an established system of land ownership and management which has prevailed for centuries. Use every means possible and every potential ally to achieve your end.'

Contacts

Dr Michael Foxley
Secretary

Tresiaig and Achaphubuil Crofters Woodland Trust
2 Achaphubuil
By Fort William PH33 7AL

Email:
drmichael.foxley.cllr@highland.gov.uk

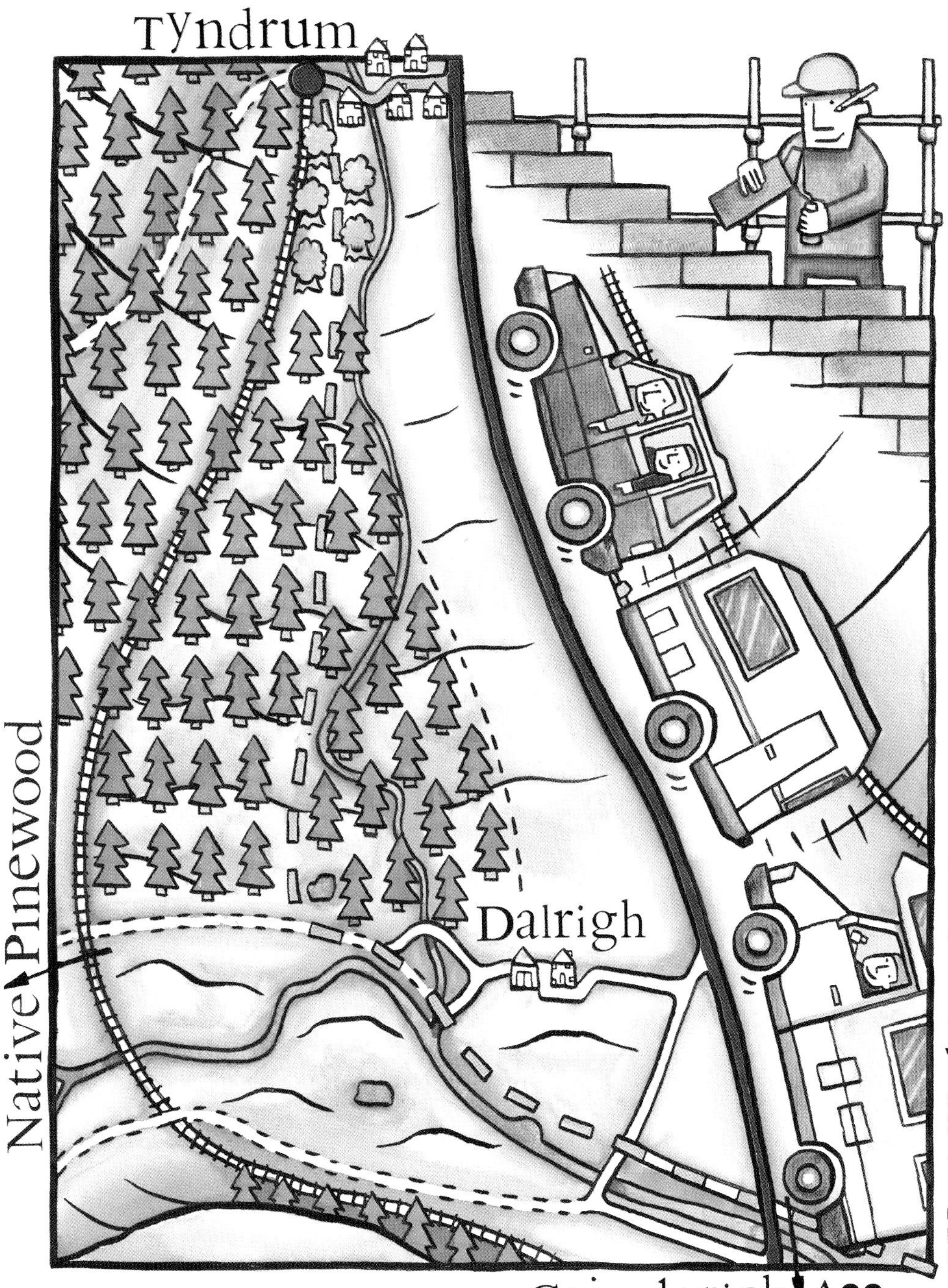

Summary

- Tyndrum Community Woodland is located between Tyndrum and Crianlarich.
- The woodland occupies 90 hectares of burned plantation replanted with Caledonian pine and native broadleaves.
- Management is through a long term lease from Forest Enterprise.
- The project is run by Tyndrum Community Woodland group, part of the Strathfillan Community Development Trust.
- The Trust is a company limited by guarantee with charitable status.
- The key aim is to encourage visitors to linger longer and support the local economy.
- The woodland was identified in 1997.

Tyndrum

Why? Tyndrum Community Woodland forms part of a larger regeneration project for Strathfillan- the area around the well known Highland communities of Tyndrum and Crianlarich. The project is run by the Strathfillan Community Development Trust and began when the Strathfillan Community Council (CC) was formed in 1991, splitting off from the Killin and Strathfillan Community Council. The new community council immediately started developing initiatives, such as providing affordable housing, to improve the well-being of the people in the area. Other initiatives are aimed at encouraging tourists to stay a little longer (and spend a little more money) in the area rather than passing through. This is an important tourist area and many of the local people are employed in the service sector.

Who? The project is for the local community as defined by the Strathfillan CC. This is taken to include visitors/ tourists as well as residents as one group depends very much upon the other. The resident population is 360, 120 of whom are members of the Trust. The community appears to be very cohesive and the two villages are closely linked together.

The core members of the Trust overlap with the Community Council and include hotel owners, landowners, Scottish Agricultural College staff and forestry contractors. The Trust, which is a company limited by guarantee with charitable status, has recently appointed a full-time Development Officer, Jennifer Marshall. Jennifer is herself local to the area. The two community woodland projects (Crianlarich has its own smaller community woodland) have their own sub-groups. The Tyndrum Community Woodland group is chaired by John Riley and has six members. The members are Directors of the Trust and co-optees. Each year the Trust must hold an AGM and there is the usual rotational standing down and election of Directors.

What ? The community woodland is located to the south-east of the village, adjacent to the A82 which links the two villages. It occupies 90 hectares of hillocky land formed from glacial debris. Formerly the area had been planted with Sitka spruce by the Forestry Commission. The plantation was just becoming well established when a fire, starting possibly on the West Highland Way, destroyed most of the plantation. About half of the area has regenerated or has recently been replanted using Caledonian pine and native broadleaves. A native pinewood remnant is located very close to the community woodland. Due to the nature of the ground there is a great diversity of habitats from rocky knolls to small lochans within the woodland. There is a good road system already in place and the footpath network is to be greatly expanded. The objective for the woodland itself is to create a multi-benefit native woodland.

Vision? The vision for the whole project is for a regenerated Strathfillan, brought about through increased local control and influence over local land, resource use and housing in order to create opportunities for locals and visitors alike. The ways in which this regeneration will be brought about are through:

- creating more affordable housing for local people
- increasing leisure and recreational opportunities for visitors and locals
- boosting the local economy
- improving the natural and physical environment and making the area more attractive

Tyndrum Community Woodland has been identified as one of several ways of encouraging visitors to come to Strathfillan. Outdoor tourism is seen as key to this. Already the West Highland Way passes through the glen and there are 14 Munros in the area. The proposed Loch Lomond and Trossachs National Park lies immediately to the south.

The specific objectives for the community woodland are:

1. To encourage more people to visit our area, to stay for longer rather than pass through and to spend more in the local economy.
2. To develop a community woodland planted with native species, such as Caledonian pine.
3. To offer a range of recreational opportunities through footpath, interpretation and picnic sites.
4. To develop a natural habitat to encourage the proliferation of wildlife.
5. To encourage the active participation of voluntary labour in planting trees, creating footpaths and other work.
6. To prepare interpretation and promotional information about the woodlands to attract locals and visitors alike.

Local jobs are seen to be very important and part of a 'do it ourselves' philosophy which runs through the project. There is a perceived need to be in control of those factors which affect the lives of people living in the community.

How? Since the Strathfillan CC split off in 1991, there has been a great enthusiasm in the local community for projects to better the area and to bring the two communities of Tyndrum and Crianlarich closer together. One of the most important projects is to develop affordable housing for local people. To this end, the community entered into discussions with Scottish Homes which introduced them to the Corrom Trust in May 1995. The Corrom Trust is a national charity with the aim of promoting community based rural regeneration. Its regeneration team worked with local people to develop the Strathfillan Regeneration Strategy, part of which was a vision for the future. One element of this was the development of a community woodland. To enable the regeneration strategy to be realised, the Strathfillan Community Development Trust was established in May 1997. Seventy people attended this first meeting.

Around about the same time, the burnt Sitka plantation immediately to the south of Tyndrum was identified as a possible site for the Tyndrum Community Woodland. The Millennium Forest for Scotland Trust was looking for projects and acted as a catalyst for the project. There was a meeting with Chris Ryder of Forest Enterprise (FE) and negotiations began. At first purchase was the Trust's favoured option but it gradually became apparent that a long term lease from FE would be more appropriate. A plan of operations was developed with input from specialists with forestry, landscape and interpretation skills. Fencing and planting began in spring 1999 and footpath works in 2000.

The biggest **challenges** have been to do with bureaucracy-

- The effort required to get approval under the Woodland Grant Scheme
- The failure to obtain certain grants (MFST & Rural Challenge) at first time of asking
- Slow progress in obtaining a legal lease agreement

The **solution** is persistence and luck

Greatest achievements? To have got this far and, particularly, to have put the necessary funding package together. The most challenging part has been dealing with the range of different organisations, each with its own objectives, way of working and timescale of decision making. It was described as similar to being at the hub of a bicycle wheel with each spoke radiating out to a different organisation and when the tension changes in one, they all have to be readjusted.

Sources of help and advice? Already within the Trust and the Community Woodland group is a high level of business and land management skills. Specialist skills in ecological survey, landscape design, woodland establishment and interpretation are being brought in. As time goes on, local people will become skilled in all areas and the need to bring in specialists will decrease. Much of the practical work to date has been carried out by outside contractors, an unfortunate necessity dictated by the timescales of some of the funding bodies. The project will be 'brought back to the community'.

Top of the list of helpful organisations is the Corrom Trust which worked well with local people and partner organisations, clarified issues and brought ideas forward. Forest Enterprise proved to be very helpful, although the Forestry Commission as a whole was not regarded as being very community orientated at that time. The Stirling Assembly (initiated, but not owned by Stirling Council) is regarded as being significant and a way of giving communities some influence in regional policy making.

The main funders to date have been Millennium Forest for Scotland Trust, the Rural Challenge Fund, Forestry Commission (WGS), SNH, Stirling Council and local businesses. Fundraising has been difficult.

A little training in management planning and chainsaw operation has been provided by MFST.

Future Activities? The establishment period for the Community Woodland runs to 2004 and there will be ongoing work beyond that date. The trees may be planted, but the bulk of the access work- footpaths, parking and interpretation remains to be done. There are some intriguing possibilities for the lease or purchase of other land and woodland in the area. This would greatly increase the value of the Community Woodland to the local people.

There is no end point to the project. It goes on forever, developing as the community develops and at a level consistent with the energy available at the time. New active group members are brought on board as they appear and this process is aided by the democratic structure of the Trust.

Lessons for others? John Riley, the chairman of the Trust and the Community Woodland group summarised the lessons from the project as the 6 Ds-

- Democracy
- Decisions – decide and agree what you are trying to achieve as a community
- Delegation – in order to carry the work forward on a broad front and not rely upon one or two individuals
- Dedication – you've got to have a passion for it
- Determination – provides motivation to overcome obstacles
- Demonstration – you need to be seen to be getting somewhere 'scalps on the belt'

Contacts

John Riley

Strathfillan Community
Development Trust
Burnside Cottage
Tyndrum
Perthshire FK20 8RY

Wooplaw

Summary

- Wooplaw is in the Scottish Borders, six miles north of Galashiels.
- The woodland is 23 hectares, of varied ages and species, conifers and broadleaves, native and exotic.
- The woodland is owned by a community group.
- Borders Community Woodlands owns and manages the woodland.
- BCW is a charitable trust.
- The key aims are the promotion of community involvement, training and education.
- The project began in 1986.

Wooplaw

Why? The project originated in 1985 with Tim Stead, a sculptor of wood and furniture maker, who lived and worked in the Scottish Borders. He had decided (initially for aesthetic reasons) to use only native British timber and this led on to the idea of wanting to find a way to help to restore this resource as well as use it. He came up with the idea of 'Axes for Trees' and produced 365 handmade hardwood axe heads- one for each day of 1986. These would be sold to raise money to buy a piece of land on which trees could be planted.

The publicity for this scheme drew the attention of two people involved in the native and community woods movement in Scotland, Donald McPhillimy and Alan Drever. They met with Tim in 1987 and together discussed the possibility of creating a community woodland. This led to the formation of Borders Community Woodlands (BCW) to take the project forward and a large public meeting in Melrose, in which David Bellamy participated.

Fortuitously, a local 23 ha woodland called Wooplaw came on the market and within 3 months BCW had succeeded in securing sufficient donations and grants to top up the axe head money and purchase the first community woodland of its type in the UK.

Who? Due to Wooplaw's rural location between several communities, BCW is a community of local interest rather than belonging to any one community. Most members come from the surrounding towns and villages of Melrose, Galashiels, Tweedbank, Stow, Lauder, Blainslie and Earlston but the membership extends much more widely.

The beneficiaries are all the people who use the woodland for a wide range of activities and for training/educational purposes. Members also have access to products from the woodland (e.g. firewood and willows). A large number of local groups and schools use it on a regular basis. It serves as the base for the local WATCH group (the junior arm of the Scottish Wildlife Trust). The Prince's Trust run two week team building exercises in the woodland and Earlston High School use it annually as a base for their third year studies. A great deal of training in woodland management skills has taken place at Wooplaw which has led to several of the trainees finding full time employment. Timber has been sold and contractors employed, all contributing to the local economy and rural development.

For the first few years the project was run by the original core group of 6-7 people. There are now approximately 120 members who each pay £5 for 2 years membership. Members' meetings, which are open to all, are held monthly in the log cabin in the woodland. Those who attend regularly (about 10 people) constitute the management committee and are given the title of Warden. They make the major decisions about management projects, events and work days. Walks through the woodland are then arranged for members who wish to have these decisions explained to them. Two newsletters per year provide details of all events and decisions. Events are well publicised in local newspapers.

Seven years after BCW was started, and mainly because of the potential availability of Lottery funding through the Millennium Forest for Scotland, another related organisation was launched called the Borders Forest Trust (BFT). Its aim is to develop the community woodland movement in the Borders region and in particular to promote the use and therefore value of native timber. This has taken off with great success and now oversees an impressive range of woodland, timber and educational projects, including a further 15 community woodlands. Of particular relevance is the ambitious Woodschool, a training centre and base for craftsmen in native timber.

Although BCW is autonomous, there is a link with BFT and its community woodland projects. This has helped in terms of being able to raise the profile of Wooplaw and place it in a wider context as a practical demonstration of managing a community woodland. BFT fundraising has also provided access to additional funding for BCW. Wooplaw in turn has been important to BFT as a well developed community woodland and has been used to demonstrate what is possible to each of the new community woodland projects. It has also been a source of experienced trainees, some of whom are now in full time employment delivering other BFT projects. However, there is some concern that that the unique BCW identity has, to a certain extent, been lost in the wider project.

What? Wooplaw (originally Uplaw, or Hill of the Curlew) is the collective name for a group of 8 linked woodlands totalling 23 hectares (56 acres) situated in the Scottish Borders 6 miles north east of Galashiels. The woodlands are in two clusters and were part of a designed landscape around Wooplaw House. Wooplaw is classified as a mixed 'long established' woodland of plantation origin and is growing on mainly brown earths and surface water gleys. It lies at an elevation of between 230 and 280 m above sea level, on a ridge which forms part of the foothills of the Moorfoot hills. It is relatively susceptible to windthrow (Hazard class 5). A stream, the Allen Water, flows through parts of the woodlands.

While an initial survey revealed that there were no special habitats or species and few ancient woodland indicators, the woodland supports a surprisingly wide diversity of flora and fauna. This is due to the fact that there are many small stands with a considerable mixture of sizes and ages. General proportions of species are: exotic conifer 55%, native broadleaves 23%, native conifer 18%, exotic broadleves 4%. One of the distinctive characteristics of the woodland is an area of big (140 year old) Sitka spruce and Douglas fir. Apart from the new planting, the age of the trees in the other compartments varies between 30-80 years. Species include birch, ash, oak, lime, willow, sycamore, Sitka spruce, Scots pine, larch, Western red cedar and Douglas fir.

Little work had been done in the woodland for about 15 years before it was bought by BCW. The 23 ha included three unplanted fields which have now added an additional 9.3ha of largely native broadleaved woodland (Axehead Wood, Gullet Wood and South Gullet Wood).

Vision? The original objectives of Borders Community Woodlands were:

- An educational resource for children and adults
- A place for peaceful enjoyment and relaxation
- A practical local response to concern about international exploitation of forests
- An opportunity to learn about forest products
- Scope for trying out different management practices especially those that encourage native trees and a habitat favourable for wildlife.

These objectives largely remain. Added to them are the promotion of the concept of community woodlands, the provision of disabled access, the enhancement of wildlife habitats and the promotion of training and education.

The 3rd 5 year management plan has now been prepared. The general aims are now defined as long term restructuring towards native woodland and continuing to promote community involvement, training and education.

How? The 'Axes for Trees' proved very successful in demonstrating serious commitment to potential funders, attracted members and undoubtedly helped the project get off to a good start.

- An MSc student from the University of Edinburgh, John Sargeant, was inspired by the project and decided to base his dissertation on it. In 1989 BCW gained access to a comprehensive survey with management recommendations which still form the basis for planning future management.
- The first Forestry Commission (FC) planting grant was applied for shortly after this and after some discussion, a Community Woodland Supplement was also made available.
- However, the busy people who were involved initially got on with being busy elsewhere and the initial enthusiasm began to wane. For the next three years a small core of the original instigators laboured doggedly with very little help. They managed to plant the two smaller fields (the Gullet Woods) and carry out some essential management, drainage and access works.
- Over this period, markets for wood products (small coppice material and firewood) were developed. Income was used to fund the development of the group and buy necessary equipment.
- In 1993 one of the core members, Hugh Chalmers, who was working with the Scottish Wildlife Trust (SWT) began to bring teams of volunteers to the site for their practical training. Axehead Wood was fenced and planted. As labour costs were very low, it was possible to spread the grant money over a wide range of operations. During this period the log cabin was built and a tree nursery and holding area constructed.

- 1993 also saw the start, with woodland craft days, of the many diverse community events which are now held regularly in the woodland and which bring in volunteers to help with the work.
- In 1994 horse logging demonstrations were held and schools became more closely involved through a local head teacher who had come onto the committee. This year saw the start of the annual Hallowe'en party, winter tree dressing, tree planting events, charcoal making demonstrations and a woodland dance performance.
- In 1996 £10,000 was awarded by the Charities Lottery Foundation for access and a pond with dipping platform, otter holt, otter hide, bridge and a thatched shelter were built in Gullet Wood. SNH also supported this work.
- In 1997 Wooplaw was the setting for several ambitious arts projects including a night-time film performance "Beasts of the Forest" and a sculpture project. A schools education pack was produced. This was supplied to all schools in the Borders and is still used regularly by them and by the Borders Council Ranger Service .
- 1998 saw the launch of the Woodland Access Initiative. 800 metres of all ability access trails were constructed with interpretative maps, as well as an outdoor classroom, educational resource box, composting toilet and green woodworking area. There has been close liaison with local disabled groups and for two years they were coming out on a regular basis to help in the construction of the new facilities. Mazda and Future Forests funded the planting of a further 600 trees in shelters as part of a carbon fixation deal.
- In 1999, 1000 willows were planted in Gullet Wood as a source of native and basket willows to provide adequate material for local willow crafts courses. The SWT group is visiting less often using the woodland mainly for training in habitat mapping and bird identification.

BCW believes that there have been no significant **obstacles** in developing Wooplaw. The principal problem was the initial falling off of enthusiasm in the early years. This was due partly to the woodland being at a distance from any one community and partly due to naivety. For example, all the teachers in the region were invited to an open event one Saturday shortly after the project's launch, but none turned up. The project was right, but the triggers for action and timing were not. There were a number of key factors which acted as **solutions** and rekindled the enthusiasm which has been maintained ever since. One of these was the regular involvement of the SWT habitat management team, members of which developed enthusiasm and commitment that was carried beyond working hours. Another was the involvement of a new 'generation' of people mainly from Stow and Lauder including local head teacher, Jeanette Fox, now Secretary of BCW, who was instrumental in forging the right kind of links with local schools.

It was recognised that it is crucial to maintain a core of committed members. This is achieved by deliberately seeking out people likely to be interested, by maintaining their interest through varying ideas and activities and by ensuring that everyone has a real sense of reward for services rendered. There have been no major disagreements between core members and no major crises.

Vandalism has been a minor problem. The wood stove has twice been stolen from the hut and at one point a group of young people from the other side of the Firth of Forth decided it would be a lovely setting for their weekend raves.

Greatest Achievements? Probably due to the fact the BCW is a pioneering project it has generated, and tolerated, a great deal more publicity than might otherwise have been the case. This has been deliberately fostered (e.g. via display boards circulated round Scotland) to promote the concept of community woodlands.

The project has received a huge stream of visitors from all over the world and from a wide range of professional and academic organisations. BCW also deals with constant enquiries from other groups which see it as a project worthy of emulation. BCW is proud to be "a bunch of amateurs" whose advice is being sought.

Regular small but significant successes have been the events and televised news items such as the opening of the access trail in September 1999. Possibly the only challenge currently facing the group is maintaining its identity alongside Borders Forest Trust and this is being discussed amicably.

Sources of help and advice? Skills within the group at the outset were habitat management and practical forestry. Tim Stead was very good at marketing and promotion and was able to access administrative support. More recently the group has had access through its members to a wide range of knowledge and contacts in education, the arts, timber crafts and habitat management. Chainsaw training for wardens has been provided and funded by Scottish Borders Enterprise.

Early inspiration and help came from the alternative forestry movement in Scotland, the Laggan project and Reforesting Scotland. The first organisations to provide funding and support were the Worldwide Fund for Nature, the Countryside Commission for Scotland and the Marks Trust. This was followed by the Forestry Commission's grants and help from SNH for tools and habitat creation. The regular input of labour from SWT training teams has been very significant. There has been a steady income from a wide range of small grants such as Shell Better Britain, BT Access for All and Borders Regional Council.

A proportion of funding is now accessed through BFT and some discrete projects are also implemented by BFT. Regular sources of income are Woodland Management Grant, timber sales and donations made at events. Timber was originally felled and converted by members, but this was considered to be too time consuming and is now undertaken by contractors, thereby supporting the local economy.

Future Activities? In general terms, the aim is to manage according to the management plan and to continue to provide and promote all the community benefits. There are no immediate plans to expand the woodland beyond its existing size. Two specific aims for the future are to widen the diversity of land use and the number of useful products from the woodland.

The new willow nursery/coppice area at Gullet Wood is to be expanded by the planting of a further 4000 sets, bringing the total area up to 1 acre. Other ideas which have been discussed include the production of birch sap wine, fungi harvesting, planting fruit trees and bushes and the development of charcoal production.

Discussions are also being held on a possible name change, from Borders Community Woodlands to Wooplaw Community Woodland in order to avoid the current confusion with BFT.

Lessons for others? The main lessons are:

- Have a long term vision
- Have patience in achieving it
- Realise there is a lot to learn and don't hesitate to ask advice
- Get involved in the movement generally and develop a common purpose

Contacts

Angela Mercer
Chair

Borders Community Woodland
Harryburn Stables
Lauder TD2 6PD

Section 3: RDF Toolbox of Resources

General Information and Encouragement

Handbooks

Community Woodland Handbook
Reforesting Scotland

A handbook aimed at both community woodland groups and agencies with an interest in increasing community participation. Headings include – Getting Organised, Involving More People, How to Learn new Skills, How to Learn from other Community Woodlands and How to Stay Healthy and Safe.
£4.50 plus £1 p&p.

Available from: Reforesting Scotland, 62-66 Newhaven Road,
Edinburgh EH6 5BQ

Phone: 0131 554 4321 • Fax: 0131 554 0088
Email: info@reforestingscotland.org
Website: www.reforestingscotland.org

Involving Communities in Forestry (Practice Guide 10)
Forestry Commission (1996)

Written from the agency perspective, this guide considers the range of community woodlands with an emphasis on the more urban end of the spectrum. There are several interesting short case studies at the end.

Available from: Forestry Commission, Publications, PO Box 100, Fareham,
Hampshire PO14 2SX

Phone: 01329 331345 • Fax: 01329 330034
Email: reception@telelink.co.uk
Website: www.forestry.gov.uk

Grants for Tr££s
Calderdale Metropolitan Borough Council (1996)

An excellent guide to all tree planting and woodland management grants with sources of advice.

Available from: Calderdale MBC, Leisure Services Dept., Wellesley Park, Halifax, W Yorkshire
HX2 0AY

Phone: 01422 359454

Guide to Planning a Community Tree Planting Scheme
National Forest

This little booklet was issued in the early days of the National Forest. It gives very basic advice on where trees might be planted, how to choose trees and how to go about planting them. One or two (possibly out of date) local contacts are provided. An updated version 'Every Tree Counts' has been recently produced and is likely to be more relevant.

Available from: The National Forest, Enterprise Glade, Bath Lane, Moira, Swadlincote,
Derbyshire DE12 6BD

Phone: 01283 551 211

Community Orchards

Common Ground (1999)

This booklet offers ways of saving old orchards and opportunities to plant new ones, for the enjoyment of the community, as a reservoir for local varieties of fruit and a refuge for wildlife. £1

Available from: Common Ground, PO Box No 25309,
London NW5 1ZA

Phone: 0171 267 2144.
E-mail: info@commonground.org.uk
Website: www.commonground.org.uk

Hands on Scotland

Scottish Conservation Projects Trust (1996)

This is an excellent guide to organising a conservation group with a lot of information which will be useful to RDF groups. Some sections are quite short but to the point. In addition there 13 case studies, technical notes on conservation operations, sample constitutions and risk assessments and a good list of contacts.

Available from: SCPT, Balallan House, 24 Allan Park, Stirling FK8 2QG

Phone: 01786 479697 • Fax: 01786 465359
E-mail: scotland@btcv.org.uk
Website: www.btcv.org.uk

Crofter Forestry

Crofters Commission

Summarises the legal aspects of crofter forestry and describes the design process.

Available from: Crofter Commission, 4/6 Castle Wynd, Inverness IV2 3EQ

Phone: 01463 663450 • Fax: 01463 711820
Email: crofters_commission@cali.co.uk

Crofter Forestry Experiences

Scottish Crofters Union (1996)

A review of progress in crofter forestry up to the time of publication complete with 11 examples of crofting townships' experiences. It also places Crofter Forestry in context and provides much useful information and contacts.

Available from: SCU, Old Mill, Broadford, Isle of Skye IV49 9AQ

Phone: 01471 822529 • Fax: 01471 822799
Email: scu@sprite.co.uk

The Crofting Forestry Handbook

Scottish Crofters Union (1993)

The definitive practical guide to establishing and managing small woodlands in the Highlands and Islands.

Available from: SCU (details above)

Community Woodland Resource Pack

Woodland Trust

Advice on many aspects of community woodlands.

Available from: Woodland Trust, Autumn Park, Grantham, Lincs. NG31 6LL

Phone: 01476 581111 • Fax: 01476 590808

Woodland Owners Handbook

Coed Cymru (1998)

Designed for owners of native (farm) woodlands, the handbook provides information on silviculture, conservation, timber properties of native and exotic trees, timber conversion and seasoning and markets and marketing. Shortly to be replaced by individual factsheets.

Available from: Coed Cymru, The Old Sawmill, Tregynon, Newtown, Powys SY16 3PL

Phone: 01686 650777 • Fax: 01686 650696
Email: coedcymru@mid-wales.net
Website: www.coedcymru.mid-wales.net

Videos

Wild about Woodlands

Central Scotland Countryside Trust (1999)

A well made inspirational video extolling the virtues of community woodlands (rather than RDF) in central Scotland, told mainly through the words of local people.

Available from: CSCT, Hillhouseridge, Kirkwood, Shotts, Lanarkshire ML7 4JS

Phone: 01501 822015 • Fax: 01501 823919
Website: www.csct.co.uk

A Woodland Journey and Coppice Woodlands into the Next Millennium

Carers of Woodland

The first video takes the viewer through an ancient woodland exploring its biodiversity. The second discusses issues related to the management and value of woodlands. £7 plus £1 p&p.

Available from: Carers of Woodland, Weathersfield Arts Centre, Weathersfield, Braintree, Essex CM7 4EQ

Phone: 01371 851054
Email wac100647@aol.com.uk
Website: www.carersofwoodland.freeserve.co.uk

Woods for All

Reforesting Scotland

Deals with the issues of improving access and opportunities for people with disabilities.

Available from: Reforesting Scotland (details above)

Websites

British Trees
www.british-trees.com

A collection of reference material from within and outwith the UK which includes a native tree guide, bibliography and magazine list, list of organisations and photo collections plus links to other useful sites.

Royal Forestry Society
www.rfs.org.uk

Includes an electronic searchable version of its excellent publication- Grants, Loans, Sponsorship and Advice on Trees and Woodlands in the UK.

Rurale
www.nrec.org.uk

Excellent source of information on key players in UK rural development.

Trees of Time and Place
www.totap.org.uk

Explains the Trees of Time and Place project with information on the history of woodlands and seed collection.

Woodlander
www.woodlander.co.uk

A self styled "forestry, woodland and arboriculture database for the UK" which provides suppliers of tools, materials and equipment, timber purchasers, training providers and a range of useful links.

Woodnet
www.woodnet.org.uk

Good for networking advice and timber marketing.

Existing Case Studies and Research

Scottish Rural Development Forestry Programme

Reforesting Scotland

The results of the very influential SRDFP are held for reference by Reforesting Scotland which was one of the three partners in the programme. There are accompanying videos and annual reports.

Unavailable except for reference from Reforesting Scotland.

Various Studies

Arkleton Centre

The Arkleton Centre has published several relevant titles including:

'Social and Development Forestry Issues in Rural Economies'
'The Potential for Community Participation in Forest Management in Remote Rural Areas'
'Forming Effective Rural Partnerships'

A full list is available from: Arkleton Centre, University of Aberdeen, St Mary's, Elphinstone Road, Aberdeen AB24 3UF

Phone: 01224 273 901
Email ark030@abdn.ac.uk
Web site: www.abdn.ac.uk/arkleton

Directory

Cheltenham Observatory

Cheltenham Observatory is building a directory of 50 case studies of sustainable rural initiatives which includes woodland projects such as Tinker's Bubble, Oswestry Hills Woodland Initiative, Woodworks, and other projects which may have useful lessons in terms or approach and organisation.

Available from: Cheltenham Observatory, Francis Hall Close, Swindon Road, Cheltenham, Glos. GL50 4AZ

Phone: 01242 544 082
Email: observatory@chelt.ac.uk
Website: www.chelt.ac.uk

Project Profiles

Millennium Forest for Scotland Trust

MFST can provide information on the projects it has funded, of which about 10 could be described has having an element of RDF. A Millennium Award has also been awarded to an individual to research 15 community woodlands throughout the UK.

Available from: MFST, 91 Mitchell St., Glasgow G1 3LN

Phone: 0141 229 2001 • Fax: 0141 204 2222
Email: communications@milleniumforest.com
Website: www.millenniumforest.com

Social Land Ownership

Not for Profit Landowners Group (1998)

Eight case studies from north Scotland including the inspirational Assynt experience, several of which have a forestry element. Written by those involved.

Available from: NFP, c/o RSPB, Etive House, Beechwood Business Park, Inverness IV2 3BW

Phone: 01463 715000 • Fax: 01463 715315

Woodland Initiatives Register

National Small Woods Association (1998)

A comprehensive guide to 98 initiatives throughout the UK arranged as single woodland, local, regional, global and national initiatives and professional organisations.

Available from: NSWA, 3 Perkins Beach Dingle, Stiperstones, Shropshire SY5 0PF

Phone: 01743 792644 • Fax: 01743 792655

Community Woodlands Case Studies

Central Scotland Countryside Trust (1999)

A series of four case studies of community woodlands, with an urban emphasis. Three are in central Scotland and one in Yorkshire.

Available from: CSCT (details above)

First Nation Forestry Program Annual Report

First Nation Forestry Program (1998)

Fascinating description of North American first nation woodland initiatives, most of which could be classified as RDF.

Available from: First Nation Forestry Program

Web Site: www.fnfp.gc.ca

Community

Community Woodland Handbook

Reforesting Scotland

A handbook aimed at both community woodland groups and agencies with an interest in increasing community participation. Headings include- Getting Organised, Involving More People, How to Learn new Skills, How to Learn from other Community Woodlands and How to Stay Healthy and Safe.

Available from: Reforesting Scotland (details above)

Forests for Real

Forest Enterprise Fort Augustus

Developed by FE staff, this is similar to the Planning for Real planning exercise, set up as a hands on activity to increase involvement by a wide range of local people. It is tried and tested in this forest district.

Available on loan from: Malcolm Wield, Forest Enterprise, Strathoich, Fort Augustus, Inverness-shire PH32 4BT

Phone: 01320 366322 • Fax: 01320 366581
Email: fort.aug.fd@forestry.gov.uk

Community Woodland Handbook

Reforesting Scotland

A handbook aimed at both community woodland groups and agencies with an interest in increasing community participation. Headings include- Getting Organised, Involving More People, How to Learn new Skills, How to Learn from other Community Woodlands and How to Stay Healthy and Safe.

Available from: Reforesting Scotland (details above)

Woodlands

British Trust for Conservation Volunteers (1997)

An old favourite- all you need to know about the practical management of woodlands with hand tools with a good deal of conservation theory mixed in for good measure. BTCV publish many other practical guides at a level suitable for trained volunteers.

Available from: BTCV Enterprises, The Conservation Centre, Balby Road, Doncaster DN4 0RH

Phone: 01302 859522 • Fax: 01302 310167

Forestry Publications

Forestry Commission

The Forestry Commission has published a vast range of publications, many of which will be of use to RDF groups. Particularly relevant are Handbook 6 Forestry Practice and Handbook 9 Growing Broadleaves for Timber.

Available from: Forestry Commission Publications (details above)